Herbs *of the* BIBLE

2000 Years of Plant Medicine

Other related books from Interweave Press

by Steven Foster

101 Medicinal Plants: An Illustrated Guide

Herbs for Your Health

by Christopher Hobbs

Foundations of Health

Stress and Natural Healing

Women's Herbs, Women's Health, with Kathi Keville

Herbs *of the* BIBLE

.... ❧ ....

2000 Years of Plant Medicine

.... ❧ ....

JAMES A. DUKE, Ph.D.

Illustrations by Peggy Kessler Duke

Edited by Mary Ann Telatnik

INTERWEAVE PRESS

Herbs of the Bible
2000 Years of Plant Medicine

Cover design: Bren Frisch
Cover illustration: Eton College Library, Windsor (reproduced with permission from *The Illustrated Herbal*)
Editor: Mary Ann Telatnik
Page design: Dean Howes

Text copyright 1999 by James A. Duke

Illustrations:
Pages 21 and 23 Susan Strawn Bailey (copyright 1999 by Interweave Press)
Page 16 Biblioteca Nazionale Centrale, Florence (reproduced with permission from *The Illustrated Herbal*)
Page 25 The British Library, London (reproduced with permission from *The Illustrated Herbal*)
Page 27 Bibliothèque Municipale, Rouen (reproduced with permission from *The Illustrated Herbal*)
All other illustrations by Peggy Kessler Duke (copyright 1999 by Peggy Duke)

Interweave Press
201 East Fourth Street
Loveland, Colorado 80537-5655
USA

Printed in China at Midas Printing International

Duke, James A., 1929-
    Herbs of the Bible: 2000 years of plant medicine/James A. Duke.
      p. cm.
    Includes bibliographical references and index.
    ISBN 1-883010-66-7
     1. Herbs in the Bible. 2 Plants in the Bible. 3. Herbs—Therapeutic use. I. Title.

BS665 .D85 1999
220.8'58163—dc21

                                         99-046121

First printing: IWP-7.5M1099:CC

This book is dedicated to all those who are still not completely convinced that creationism nor evolutionism nor herbalism nor pharmaceutics have offered all the explicit answers often so desperately sought by those in need of physical or spiritual healing. From one still seeking answers, often in the Forest Temple or the Green Farmacy.

Preface

For there shall be a sowing of peace, the vine shall yield its fruit, the ground shall give its produce, and the skies shall give their dew. I will cause the remnant of this people to possess all these things.

Zechariah 8:12

Rationale

In my eighth decade my thoughts too often wander to religion as I contemplate the great beyond—sometimes fearfully, but more often fearlessly, anticipating nothing. In contemplating religion, I reflect on the Bible and my first book *Herbs in the Bible* (Duke and Duke, 1983). It was my third published book and is now out of print. I was wondering whether to rewrite the book when Linda Ligon and Logan Chamberlain at Interweave Press invited me to write *Herbs of the Bible: 2,000 Years of Plant Medicine*. They encouraged me to focus on 58 of the more important 141 species covered in that first version. Their enthusiasm about the project and other, personal reasons prompted me to write this new book about the medicinal plants of the Holy Land. I have been to the Holy Lands of Egypt and Israel three times since writing that first book. And I admit to feeling some mystical power as I wandered Mount Sinai, once on camelback, or the narrow streets of Jerusalem.

Purpose

As we move into the third Christian millennium, we may be ready to rekindle a medical as well as spiritual explanation of the herbs and plants that have been with us for as many as six millennia. We must not lose sight of the food, medicinal, cosmetic, or therapeutic values of these herbs and plants. Our lives may depend on it.

I wonder from time to time what our Buddhist, Moslem, or Jewish brethren, among others, think of the hoopla as Christians face a new millennium. Other religions and societies are into their third, fourth, or even fifth millennia. However, a new year,

7

a new century, and a new millennium is an opportunity for reflection and anticipation. What have we done to the earth, to its flora and fauna? To ourselves? How accurately have we measured progress in diet, medicine, and health care?

Audience

I offer this volume to all who are curious about the history and efficacy of plants and herbs mentioned in the Bible. I offer an historical perspective of these plants' healing and dietary properties within the framework of scientific verification. I leave it to you, the reader, to search and discover how these plants can enhance your own health and lives—no promises.

Content

Better is a dinner of vegetables where love is than a fatted ox and hatred with it.

Proverbs 15:17

The herbs and plants of the first millennium were already well established in the ancient Near East: Egypt, Israel, Syria. Trade with India and China and the Mediterranean was thriving. What wasn't grown in the Holy Lands was imported. It was an agricultural society. Lives revolved around the season of planting, cultivating, and harvesting. Perhaps Adam and Eve's real sin, eating from the tree of knowledge, was to put at risk a life free from the daily labor of toiling in fields and orchards, eking out a living in spite of pestilence and capricious weather. God offered them an eternal Eden if they would just be satisfied to obey Him and leave the tree alone.

The Bible mentions 128 plants that were part of everyday life in ancient Israel and its Mediterranean neighbors. The writers of the Old and New Testaments included references to plants and trees in their stories and allegories as agriculturists, not as botanists. Matching today's herbs with their exact counterparts is more difficult because of translations from Greek, Hebrew, or Aramaic to Latin and eventually to English—lots of opportunity for editorial license. Let me add that scholars don't agree on what was meant by many of the biblical plant names. Israeli authors like botanical scholar Michael Zohary, more familiar with the Israeli flora and the Bible than I am, should be better equipped to speculate as to which herbs were really meant in some elusive passages. Zohary, too, leaves a few problems unresolved. However, secular and religious scholars provide us with insight into the lives and times of those who lived, labored, and worshipped in the ancient Holy Lands.

And if botanists and biblical scholars disagree on the origins of plants in the Bible, the mystery deepens and broadens with the disagreement over which translation of the Bible to quote from—the King James version vs. Standard; Standard vs. New Revised Standard; English vs. American Standard—you get the picture. The authors, prophets, and theologians were more concerned with our souls than our botany.

I have taken the utmost care to compile the following herbs and plants and compare them with those cited in the Bible. The language of the biblical quotations speaks more to the role of the selected plant than to a faithfulness to a particular version of the Bible. Although I am especially fond of the language of Shakespeare in the King James Version I am aware of its limitations as an accurate translation of the original Bible. In fact, most biblical scholars and researchers agree that the King James version is one of the worst translations in English. Therefore, I also quote from the English, Jerome, Oxford, and New Revised Standard Versions.

In this new edition of *Herbs of the Bible*, I focus on each plant. First, I look at its ritual, medicinal, dietary, or cosmetic significance when the scriptures were written. Next, I relate the plant's role in daily life in the Holy Land and neighboring lands. Then, I list the benefits we enjoy from them today as well the findings of current medical research. Finally, I list the role these plants have played in cultures around the world from folk remedies to folklore. What continues to amaze me is how much the world's people have in common in the way each plant has been used either as food, as medicine, in religious rituals, or for beauty and health care.

The appendix contains the Latin taxonomy of the plants as well as their original Hebrew, Greek, Arabic, and Aramaic names. I believe that my enumerating the sources of research and including the plant properties can strengthen the immune systems, if not also the faith systems, of some readers, thereby helping them heal themselves. Books listed in the bibliography contain thorough and scientific discussions of the health and medicinal properties of the herbs chosen for this book. For the sake of readability I chose not to use footnotes or endnotes. But I assure you that each source of information is included in the bibliography.

In no way, however, am I recommending self-diagnosis or self-medication. I am enumerating those plants that one or another scholarly authority has considered to be a biblical plant and tabulating a few of the real and folk indications for those herbs. Only your health practitioner can advise you as to whether or not you should use these herbs in your healing. I do use herbs and believe in them.

On the banks, on both sides of the river, there will grow all kinds of trees for food. Their leaves will not wither nor their rich fruit fail, but they will bear fresh fruit every month, because the water for them flows from the sanctuary. Their fruit will be for food, and their leaves for healing.

Ezekiel 47:12

Acknowledgments

You are the light of the world. A city built on a hill cannot be hid. No one after lighting a lamp puts it under the bushel basket, but on the lampstand, and it gives light to all in the house. In the same way, let your light shine before others, so that they may see your good works and give glory to your Father in heaven.

Matthew 5:15–16

I thank Linda Ligon for sharing my vision for this book, following our great trip to the Amazon. And I extend huge thanks to the team of editorial and artistic contributors at Interweave Press—Mary Ann Telatnik, Vicki Yost, Dean Howes, Nancy Disney, and others—who from afar handled pressing issues very astutely and expeditiously, and who helped dig into new information on the biblical ideas I had overlooked.

And huge thanks to my own great team of coworkers, including my right hand of more than twenty years, Judi DuCellier, and my e-mail researchers, past and present—Mary Jo Bogenschutz-Godwin, Dr. Stephen Beckstrom-Sternberg, and Dr. C. Leigh Broadhurst, all of whom have helped so much in getting data on the biblical species into my database, www.ars-grin. gov/ duke.

And a big thanks to those who are helping me grow the medicinal herbs of the Bible—Kerrie Kyde and Ellen Gordon—for seeing to it that my Green Farmacy Garden has most of the important biblical medicinal species.

It's nice to share the title page with my postgraduate girlfriend, now my wife of all told nearly four decades, Peggy. If the picture is worth a thousand words, she has outdone me again.

Editor's acknowledgments

Many people contributed to the final draft of *Herbs of the Bible: 2,000 Years of Plant Medicine*. They generously contributed their scholarship, knowledge, and talents. Thank you.

Jackie Adolph, Dr. Frank Ames, Julie Breen, Emmalie Conner, Denver (Colorado) Botanic Gardens Library, Fort Collins (Colorado) Public Library, Rabbi Howard Hirsch, Mt. Sinai Synagog (Cheyenne, Wyoming), Laura Peterson, Jerry Peterson, Elsa Lee Sarlo, Keven Dirk Sarlo, Shepherd of the Hills Lutheran Church (Boulder, Colorado), Susan Strawn-Bailey, Donna Telatnik, Stephen C. Telatnik, Dr. Monty Wilburn, and Shirley H. Wilsey.

Table of Contents

Appendices

Herbs *of the* BIBLE

2000 Years of Plant Medicine

Spain or Provence, mid-14th century butcher's broom *(Ruscus aculeatus),* bitter apple *(Citrullus colocynthis),* cassia *(cassia senna), and* dodder *(Cuscuta sp.).*

Introduction

We credit our ancestors with learning which plants were edible or poisonous. Trial and error, intuition, and observation allowed the human species to survive and thrive on the nutritious vegetables, fruits, and grains that nature provided. We believe this because we are here. Yet today, as a society, we're skeptical about our ancestors' knowledge of which plants had medicinal virtues. The medical community is quick to dismiss such time-honored remedies as onion plasters for colds or garlic for high blood pressure as "old wives' tales," simply because modern science has not gotten around to verifying their worth.

The empirical proof is there. We experience the sleep-enhancing effect of a cup of chamomile tea or the healing effect on a sore throat of a spoonful of elderberry syrup. We note the sinus relief we may feel if we take a tincture of ephedra or the energy boost we experience by taking Siberian ginseng over time. We observe that aromatherapy and essential oils used in massage therapy alter moods for the better and enhance healing, both physical and psychological. Modern science has, in fact,

validated the medicinal value of many of these herbal remedies. Yet the modern medical community remains skeptical.

Doctors still warn that herbs should not be used as medicines because dosage levels haven't been established. They caution that if the benefits of an herb haven't been proven, then that herb might be harmful. Too often, the scientific community considers an herb guilty until proven innocent, as it were. It's true that we can't prove how many times herbs have saved lives in recent years, but data published in *The Journal of the American Medical Association* (JAMA) between 1997 and 1998 indicates that FDA-approved prescription drugs have killed between 100,000 and 150,000 in the United States alone. I rest my case. It simply makes good sense to give respectful attention to the plant wisdom of the ages.

PLANTS AND THE BIBLE

Recent studies strongly suggest the power of religion in medicine. While the Bible and Koran do not stress the medicinal uses of plants as much as faith in healing, both tomes are full of references to medicinal plants. Israeli botanical scholar Michael Zohary offers an insightful explanation: "Although healing by plants is not explicitly mentioned in the Bible, herbal remedies [in those times] were numerous and specific. The ultimate healer was God, and prayer was therefore the remedy most often prescribed." Because mentioning medicinal uses of plant would defy "the belief in God's exclusive healing power," they were rarely mentioned in the scripture.

Though still the subject of interpretation, biblical anthropologists have revealed another perspective on why the Bible does not include more about the medicinal benefits of herbs and plants. Because the authors of the books and scriptures just didn't know. The realm of herbs and healing belonged to women, and peasant women at that. The Old Testament authors were patriarchal males who wrote about the elite (Kings David and Solomon or tribal leaders Abraham and Jacob) for the learned, elite, patriarchal males. They may have owned land and dealt in commerce, but they belonged to an economically advantaged class and were not always in touch with the farmer in the orchard or the laborer in the field.

Through the work and physical discov-

eries of biblical scholars and anthropologists we know that the following plants did exist in ancient Israel when the books of the Bible were written: cedars; sycamore trees; the grasses emmer wheat and barley; lentils; fruit orchards consisting of almonds, figs, grapes, olives, pomegranates, and date palms. Many of the plants mentioned in this book are believed to have been cultivated in ancient Israel or in nearby countries. Carob and desert dates are all thought to have been indigenous to ancient Israel. Other food plants—apples, apricots, oranges, mulberries, walnuts, and pistachios—are thought to have been introduced through trade from more remote countries. Many drugs and spices that are mentioned in the Bible, such as spikenard, myrrh, galbanum, cinnamon, and the like, were never grown in the Middle East but were imported. The Bible mentions beans (broad beans) and vegetables (chickpeas), but bitter vetch, garden peas, and fenugreek were probably grown, too. We can only make educated guesses based on linguistics, history, and geography.

PLANT IDENTIFICATION

Zohary and other scholars point out that historical scriptures were written by people with little knowledge of botany, and translations by nonbotanists have compounded the problem. Hence the difficulties of correlating modern botanical species with plants mentioned in the Bible is overwhelming. For example, "More than seventy species of spiny plants grow among the flora of Israel and more than twenty are mentioned in the Scriptures. No other group of plant names in the Bible is so frequently misidentified and arbitrarily translated. [N]o thorn name in any version of the Bible is reliably translated."

Scholarship, both secular and religious, has opened the Levant to inspection and understanding. There is an abundance of thoughtful writing that brings the ancient peoples of the Middle East to life within the context of their socioeconomic environment, their diets and dietary laws, their rituals and celebrations, and their botany and zoology. But much of this research wasn't started until centuries after the death of Christ, millennia after the books of the Old Testament were written.

The first studies of plants in the Near East were those of the botanist Theophrastus (ca. 372-287 BC). The modern study of Egyptian flora began in 1775 by P. Forsskal during the Napoleonic expeditions. The flora of Mesopotamia, so critical to understanding the plants of biblical times, wasn't undertaken until 1867 and 1883 by Boissier and Post, respectively. The first book devoted exclusively to biblical botany was done in Latin in 1556 by Levinus Lemmens and translated twenty-one years later into English by Thomas Newton. A lot of time and history elapsed between those who wrote the Old and New Testaments and those who translated them. The first systematic study of biblical plants began with F. Hasselquist, a student of Carolus Linnaeus, the founder of modern botany.

Given this great time gap, it's only reasonable that accuracy would be lacking in the naming of ancient plants. The apple in the Garden of Eden may have been an apricot or pomegranate or orange or fig. After all, the original text refers only to the "tree of knowledge"; theologians in northern Europe gave the fruit its name many centuries later. In the Bible "bean" refers to the fava bean, and "corn" refers to wheat, yet corn, or maize, was not discovered until Columbus sailed to the New World.

Thanks to the work of biblical scholars, anthropologists, and botanists, we have good reference material for untangling some of these translation errors. We can look at a map (on page 21) of ancient Israel to understand the variety of climate and geographic conditions that influenced plant placement. The Levant stretched in a crescent around the eastern Mediterranean Sea from Turkey to the Sinai Peninsula. It includes modern Syria, Lebanon, Jordan, and Israel. Its peoples were as diverse as the geography. The Holy Land was so named by crusaders of the Christian powers when they went to the Middle East to defeat the Muslims in the 11th, 12th, and 13th centuries. The Holy Land includes the area that was Judea or Palestine (Hadrian renamed Judea after crushing the Hebrew revolt in 135 BC).

We learn that, although much of the land was desert and water rare, there were mountains, plains, and lush, green valleys. The plants varied as much as the geography and rainfall did and were as vulnerable to the impact of humans then as they are today. (Solomon ordered cedars from King Hiram of Tyre in what is now Lebanon and the forests of cedars of Lebanon were stripped to supply Solomon's building frenzy.) Egypt, Assyria, and ancient Israel all needed lumber, and the Phoenicians and Canaanites were eager to trade. Forests of oak and other tall trees fell victim to the ax as God and the prophets eradicated the practice of tree worship. No new trees were planted; even today few remain. By the time of Christ and the writers of the New Testament, some of the few tree-shaded areas were orchards kept outside cities and areas of palms clustered around isolated wells, pools, and springs.

However, translators of the Bible in the past, in the absence of good research, often had to make educated guesses. Take the example of Jeremiah 8:22, which today reads, "Is there no balm in Gilead?" The Douay Bible, written in 1609, translated this passage as, "Is there no rosin in Gilead?" resulting in this edition being known as the Rosin Bible. The Bishop's Bible of 1568 translated the same passage as, "Is there no treacle in Gilead?" It is now known in scholarly circles as the Treacle Bible. Since there are about seventeen different plants, herbs, sap residues, and gum resins that can claim to be the balm mentioned in the Bible, treacle and rosin are not unreasonable guesses.

The authors of the books of the Old Testament lived in a Levant geographically different from the one of the New Testament,

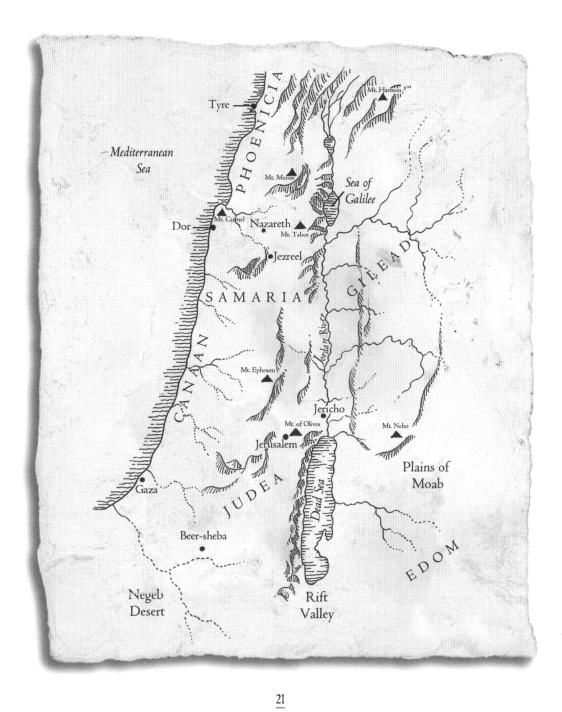

and even more different from what we today call the Holy Land. Knowing this, we can explain how there might be desert palm trees and water-dependent lilies mentioned together in the same passage. Thorn or bramble, leek or onion, watercress or endive: The plant was not critical to the story, but the lesson to be learned was.

PLANT AND POPULATION MIGRATION

The Holy Land lies at the crossroads of the African, European, and Asian continents, serving as a bridge from Egypt in northern Africa to Europe, the Middle East, and Asia. The map on page 23 illustrates the migration and trade routes that passed through ancient Israel. One view of anthropologists and archeologists, which I personally accept, is that humankind originated in Africa some four million years ago. Thus, African populations have had four million years to adapt to plants that our ancestors in the Rift Valley may have consumed in the ancient past in their quest for sustenance. It's also believed that migrating groups left by way of this landbridge one or two million years ago, some settling in Europe, some in Asia, and some reaching North America by way of Asia only about 25,000 years ago.

According to this premise, Asians have had fifty times longer than Native Americans to adapt to their indigenous plant foods and medicines, while the peoples of Africa have had a hundred times longer to coexist with theirs.

The Levant marks the most likely "checkpoint" through which population groups passed as they migrated in various directions. This geographical crossroads was also an ecological crossroads, where rainforest and desert peoples funneled in to meet people of the plains and mountains. Thus, the medicinal plants of ancient Israel, and the medicinal wisdom of early Arabs, Copts, Hebrews, and Moslems assume great importance because of their empirical antiquity.

The migratory patterns of herbs and plants follow those of the people who relied on them, uncertain what they would find at the end of their journeys. As people, families, and societies moved they took with them cuttings, seeds (both intentionally and unintentionally as seed husks clung to clothes and packings), or saplings of plants and herbs necessary for their well-being or in accordance with God's directives. According to the Bible, Abraham's grandson Jacob immigrated into Egypt when he learned that his

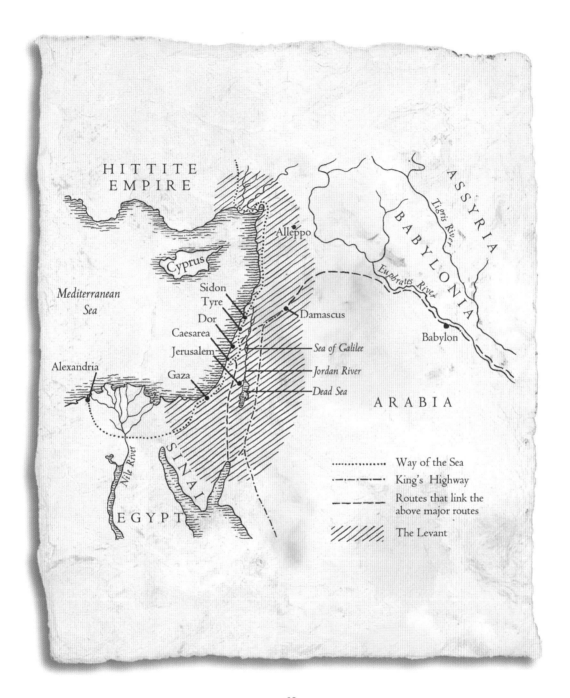

HITTITE
EMPIRE

Cyprus

Mediterranean
Sea

Sidon
Tyre
Dor
Caesarea
Jerusalem
Gaza

Alexandria

Alleppo

Damascus

Sea of Galilee

Jordan River

Dead Sea

ASSYRIA

BABYLONIA

Tigris River

Euphrates River

Babylon

ARABIA

Nile River

SINAI

EGYPT

.... Way of the Sea

—·—·—·— King's Highway

— — — — Routes that link the
above major routes

///////// The Levant

long-lost son, Joseph, was alive and prospering there. God allayed his fears in making the journey by speaking to him:

Then he said, "I am God, the God of your father; do not be afraid to go down to Egypt, for I will make of you a great nation there."

Genesis 46:3

It turned out to be a 400-year stay. In preparation Jacob took with him the saplings of acacia trees, not indigenous to Egypt. Abraham, instructed by the scriptures, had planted them in Hebron fifty years earlier in preparation for his descendants' departure from and eventual return to Hebron. Along the way on their return, they would have to build portable walls for the tabernacle in which Moses would worship on the forty-year journey home:

You shall make upright frames of acacia wood for the tabernacle.

Exodus 26:15

Now that's planning for the future! (It also helps to have a little forewarning.)

PLANTS AND HEALTH

Plants played many roles in Biblical times, just as they do today, and the definition of health can be construed broadly. Plant products all figured importantly for food, personal beauty and hygiene, and ritual and ceremony as well as for treatment of disease.

Perhaps the healthiest recommendation in the Bible is to "eat with bitter herbs," anticipating by a couple of millennia the appeal from the National Institute of Health (NIH) to eat your leafy vegetables. Though observing Jews still use bitter herbs in their Passover feast, we don't know with certainty what the bitter herbs of biblical times were. All of these bitter herbs—like chicory, dandelion, endive, lettuce, sheep sorrel, and watercress—contain many important nutrients and phytochemicals, or plant medicines. Modern agriculture has tended to select more palatable varieties and discard the more bitter ones, thus diminishing the nutritional value of these plants. Bitterness is often a strong clue that healthful compounds are present in a plant. So humankind has evolved better-tasting foods but lesser medicines. Ce-

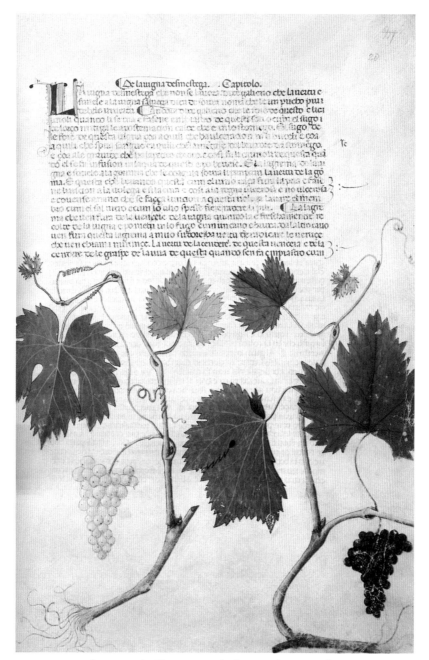

Serapion the Younger Herbolario volgare *Padua,*
1390–1400 Vine (Vitis vinifera).

25

reals, beans, fruits, and vegetables got larger, blander, more watery, and less bitter.

Agriculture has bred the medicines out of plants. Chicory, dandelion, and watercress have been supplanted by sweeter iceberg and bib lettuces. Robust broadbeans with lots of fiber and genistein and other isoflavones have been replaced with mild-flavored butterbeans and green beans, which have less. The United States Department of Agriculture (USDA) uses the term *antinutrients* to describe many of these phytomedicinal components. I suspect, and science is beginning to confirm, that including a variety of bitter herbs in one's daily diet would lower the incidence of many of the diseases that modern man is prey to.

Cosmetics, perfumes, and dyes from plants also figure in scriptures. The Song of Solomon mentions camphire, lily of the valley, rose, calamus, and cinnamon, among others, as plants used for personal fragrance. Henna was used to color the hair and decorate the body. Saffron and safflower were sources of yellow dye. Frankincense and myrrh were not only used for personal fragrance, but for burning in religious ceremonies and in preparing the dead for burial. Tragacanth and galbanum were valued aromatic gums, and myrtle appears throughout both the Old and New Testaments.

Some say that the pyramids owe their existence to the garlic- and onion-induced fortitude of the laborers, that Cicero's passion may have been in part due to the l-dopa in the fava beans he ate, that Leah was turned on by the atropine and scopolamine in the roots of the mandrake, and that the apple of the Bible may have in fact been the pomegranate, now reportedly the best plant source of the estrogen, called estrone. There's even a reference to the prophet Isaiah treating King Hezekiah's boils with fig juice. Morphine from the opium poppy was surely used as a calmative in early times. Compounds in the bitter herbs contain antiarthritic potential by virtue of their capacity to spare the destruction of collagen. Even the much-maligned dandelion is one of the best sources of lecithin. The bay leaf and its component costunolide might be viewed as possibly contributing to cancer prevention.

Western medical doctors are not generally trained in nutrition or medical alternatives, such as the use of herbs. They can't recommend what they don't know. Fortunately, more and more medical schools are recognizing the lack of nutrition and alternative medical subjects in their curricula. The traditional medical school curriculum does train

NAture f. & h. i 2·. Meluis ex eis' dulces aquo
si. Iuuamentum in egritudinibus. Nocumentu
digestioni. Remotio nocumenti cum penidiis gucha
rinis.

Ibn Botlân Tacuinum Sanitatis *Po Valley, c. 1400 Melons* (Cucumis melo).

doctors well in diagnosing and treating serious diseases. Their patients come to them for medical treatment after years of diet and substance abuse, in pain, with life-threatening diseases. So, traditionally trained doctors are suspicious of people with a holistic approach to health, people who believe in the medical power of herbs. They criticize us in part because they cannot predict the interactions of these herbs (complex mixtures of thousands of phytochemicals) with their silver bullet drugs (simplistic single synthetic or semi-synthetic chemicals). They may have forgotten that the human race has evolved with these complex holistic mixtures and not with their monochemical pills. However, western medical doctors share common ground with alternative medical practioners in one major area: the importance of practicing preventative health care. Throughout this book I stress the preventative uses of the plants from the Bible.

The major killer diseases today (cancer, cardiopathy, diabetes) may be due to replacing the high-diversity, high-fiber, high-antioxidant, low-cholesterol, holistic lifestyle of our ancestors with a sedentary, high-fat, highly refined sugar-and-flour lifestyle too often chased to excess with cigarettes and alcohol. Natural antibiotics, which we get less of in our diets today, contributed somewhat to eliminating infections. Now the lack of natural foods in our diets may be our undoing. Even though our life expectancies have nearly doubled in the century or so since we shifted away from all natural medicines, it's hard to argue that we're living better as well as living longer. Is increased life expectancy due to synthetic drugs or in spite them? Millions of dollars are spent on lowering health care costs while billions of dollars are spent on the latest and greatest silver bullets that most HMOs won't approve for treatment. Wouldn't it make more sense to spend more dollars on prevention than on drastic cures? Why aren't they emphasizing the natural, preventative healing properties of plants that USDA research has confirmed: aloes to treat radiation burns, chicory for HIV, cinnamon for diabetes, dill for colic, benzaldehyde from figs for cancer or psoralens for AIDS, garlic for hypertension, bay laurel leaves to treble insulin efficiency, scopolamine from mandrakes for vertigo, choline from nettles to prevent Alzheimer's, rosmarinic acid from hyssop's descendent oregano to prevent cataracts, anthraquinones from senna for herpes, glycoalkaloids from Sodom's apples for skin cancers, turmeric for lymphoma, walnuts to lower high cholesterol levels, yeast from the fermenting grape as a source of vitamin B-12?

Perhaps we can look forward to a millennium of enlightenment as we rediscover the power and value of herbs and other plants. The real medicinal potential of the biologically active compounds in many of these plants, combined with the advances and discoveries in modern Western medicine, offers us a healthier future in which our ancestors and our descendants share knowledge and experience. You can even start today as you flip through the following pages, based on readings from one of the most significant and venerable books in Western history. Good reading! Good health!

And Ahab spake unto Naboth, saying, Give me thy vineyard, that I may have it for a garden of herbs, because it is near unto my house; and I will give thee for it a better vineyard than it; or, if it seem good to thee, I will give thee the worth of it in money.

1 Kings 21:2

Almonds

Prunus dulcis (Mill.)

When Moses went into the tent of the covenant on the next day, the staff of Aaron for the house of Levi had sprouted. It put forth buds, produced blossoms, and bore ripe almonds.

Numbers 17:8

POSSIBLE BENEFITS

Acne	*Dermatitis*
Asthma	*Laryngitis*
Cancer	*Neuralgia*
Cough	

The Hebrew word for almonds means "diligence." The almond tree, the first tree that flowers in Palestine, became the symbol of the reemergence of the Jewish people after the destruction of the Temple—the rod or staff of Aaron in Exodus. In Numbers God had Moses collect the staffs, symbols of power and authority, from each of the twelve tribes of Israel and plant them into the ground under the tent of the covenant. The next morning Moses returned to the tent to find the rod of Aaron blooming as an almond tree. The limbs and blossoms of the almond tree became the model for the menorah. The branches end in the calyxes of the blossoms resembling the cups that hold either candles or olive oil and wicks. The ancient Israelites also valued the nuts both for food and for the oil pressed from them. They especially favored olive and almond oils for burning in ceremonial lamps and for anointing.

According to rabbinical commentary, Hebrews see the sweet and bitter almonds as a metaphor for their people, living with the bitter and the sweet. The flowering and thriving trees verify the growth and endurance of the Jews. In contrast, the bitter almond reminds them of the days of slavery and displacement.

Modern Jews in Great Britain carry branches of flowering almonds into the synagogue during spring festival. In Israel

Skin Softener with Almond Oil

Leigh Broadhurst

1/4 cup almond oil

1/4 cup aloe vera gel

1 tablespoon rose hip seed oil

2 teaspoons vitamin C powder (or grind up tablets)

5 soft gels 400 IU vitamin E (squeeze out)

8–10 soft gels of 1,000 milligrams evening primrose or borage oils (squeeze out)

8 soft gels of 10,000 IU vitamins A and D (squeeze out)

Add up to five drops or 1 teaspoon total of one or more of the following: yarrow, lavender, peppermint, chamomile, orange, comfrey, or calendula (recommend commercial glycerin-based herbals or essential oils).

Store refrigerated. Shake well before use.

children celebrate an Arbor Day carrying branches of blooming almonds. Today the almond is widespread throughout Israel and her neighbors where modern populations enjoy the green nuts as a great delicacy, just as their ancestors did. The nuts are cultivated

Hebrews see the sweet and bitter almonds as a metaphor for their people, living with the bitter and the sweet.

for the oils obtained from the kernels. The oil is used in flavoring baked goods, perfumery, and medicines as well as in candies and confectioneries.

FOLKLORE

It is a practice to plant a tree in Israel in memory of a loved one. The holocaust museum in Jerusalem is surrounded by

31

trees dedicated to those who died in concentration camps as well as to the "Righteous Gentiles" who helped Jews during World War II.

There is a legend that Charlemagne's troops' spears, made of almond wood,

sprouted in the ground overnight, shading their tents the next day.

In Tuscany, almond branches were used as divining rods to locate hidden treasure.

Aloes

Aloe vera (L.) Birm. f.

Nicodemus also, who had at first come to him by night, came bringing a mixture of myrrh and aloes about a hundred pound weight. They took the body of Jesus, and bound it in linen cloths with the spices, as is the burial custom of the Jews.

John 19: 39–40

POSSIBLE BENEFITS

Burns   *Constipation*

Cancer   *Skin Irritations*

The aloes of biblical time are very different from the aloe vera you keep on your kitchen counter. One variety of aloes produced a juice with such a bitter smell that it was little wonder Nicodemus neutralized it with a hundred pounds of myrrh. Ancient Israelites washed the bodies of their dead and wrapped them in spices and linen, giving back to the earth what the earth nurtured. The aloes juice was imported from Yemen before aloes were eventually grown in Israel.

Another aloes (*Aloe succotrina*) produced an aromatic juice used in embalming in ancient Egypt. Both were valued for soothing or beautifying the skin. The aloes juice was included in incense, perfume, lotions, and scented powder.

From biblical times to the present, aloes have been a giant among herbs and herbal medicine. Setting sail, Columbus wrote in his diary, "All is well, Aloe is on board." One company's marketing department claims that their aloes stock came over, not on the Mayflower, but "directly from the Garden of Eden." People commonly keep an aloe vera plant in the kitchen for the instant and effective treatment of burns. Just cut a portion of the leaf and apply the juice directly to the burn. It's possible to leave the unused

Aloe vera L.

Biblical Skin Cleanser for Dry or Sensitive Skin

Leigh Broadhurst

Mix together and store in a covered jar.

¼ cup rose water

¼ cup glycerin

2 tablespoons raw honey

2 tablespoons aloe vera gel

4 capsules freeze-dried royal jelly or royal jelly honey

leaf in the sun for as long as two weeks; it will rehydrate when soaked in cold water.

Fresh aloe vera juice taken internally purges the stomach and lower intestines and relieves fevers. Externally, the aloes juice, in gels with or without lanolin, treats abrasions, burns, and skin irritations. When applied to open sores, the aloe vera extract aids in healing, exhibiting anesthetic and antibacterial action, and increasing blood or lymph flow in the small vessels in the area.

Commercially, we enjoy the marriage of aloes and cactus in bubble baths, lotions, soaps, and hand and body gels. Aloes help to

heal acne. The gel is finding its way into all sorts of cosmetics, emollients, and shampoos, sometimes in combination with jojoba.

A plaster of the aloes leaf or the leaf juice is said to be a folk remedy for tumors. The root decoction has been used for stomach cancer. The USDA gets more letters about aloes as a folk remedy for skin cancer than any other species, except possibly eggplant. I am not nearly as skeptical as the FDA, whose spokesperson considers medicinal claims as "just plain fraud. There is no way they can possibly substantiate claims that aloes can cure both hernias and cancer." Is it fraudulent to claim that cancer can be helped by the anti-tumor compound aloe-emodin?

From biblical times to the present, aloes have been a giant among herbs and herbal medicine.

FOLKLORE

Caribbeans eat aloes gel for coughs and sore throats.

Curaçao natives take the aloes gel for gallbladder ailments, Jamaicans for excess bile and colds, Bahamians for edema, and Costa Ricans for whooping cough.

Aloes flesh is mixed with rum for pneumonia and with stout for jaundice in Trinidad.

Yucatecans apply heated aloes leaves to abscesses, bruises, skin inflammations, and gumboils; others apply the hot aloes flesh to sprains.

The water used for rinsing aloes is itself

used as a eyewash for the inflammation of the inner eyelid.

In India, aloes are regarded as useful for piles and rectal fissures. Aloes relieve pelvic stress and pain and uterine disorders, generally with iron and anti-flatulents.

Slukari hunters in the Congo rub their bodies with aloes gel to eliminate the human scent so that they are less likely to disturb their prey.

During cold epidemics in Lesotho, natives take a public bath in an infusion of *Aloe latifolia*.

In Egypt, the aqueous extract of aloes is sold as Aloderm™. Produced as a cream or lotion, Aloderm promotes the healing of wounds, burns, sunburn, ulcers, and skin inflammation due to exposure to X-rays or radioactive elements.

Malayans value aloes for keeping their hair in good condition. Dissolved in alcohol, aloes are used as a hair dye or to stimulate hair growth.

Venezuelans take a drop or two of the bitter yellow aloes sap "as a drastic purge."

Apples (Apricots)

Prunus armeniaca

He sustained him in a desert land, in a howling wilderness waste;
he shielded him, cared for him, guarded him as the apple of his eye.

Deuteronomy 32:10

POSSIBLE BENEFITS

Asthma	*Eye disorders*
Cancer	*Laryngitis*
Cough	*Rheumatism*

CAUTION

Poisonous

Jacob was certainly among God's chosen people if he were the apple of God's eye. David, too, prayed to God asking to be made the apple of His eye and to be delivered from his enemies and persecutors.

We say *apples*; the Bible says *apples*. However, according to the prevailing scholarship, apples were not indigenous to the Mediterranean during the writing of the Old Testament. The authors of the Bible used *fruit* generically; the fruit could even have been bitter oranges, pomegranates, or figs! Later Jewish and Christian translators named the fruit that was familiar to them. Apricots in Cypress are still known as "golden apples." Native to China, apricots have long been abundant in Israel and were most probably introduced in biblical times. However, it still seems awkward to consider someone the "apricot of one's eye."

Apricots are cultivated for the fruit, fresh or dried, made into conserves or alcoholic beverages. The kernels produce a sweet, edible oil sometimes used as substitute for almond oil. The bitter apricot kernel is highly toxic because it contains prussic acid or hydrogen cyanide. The pits contain laetrile-like compounds that can either cure or kill, depending on dosage. Expressed apricot oil is used as a pharmaceutical vehicle; it is obtained by the

Native to China, apricots have long been abundant in Israel and were most probably introduced in biblical times.

same process as bitter almond oil via destructive distillation. Pit shells have been used to prepare activated charcoal. The Egyptians sometimes used the apricot pit charcoal as an ingredient in kohl, an eyeliner and mascara.

"An apple a day keeps the doctor away." In biblical days, Solomon said, "[C]omfort me with apples for I am sick." Milton says, "The fruit of that forbidden tree whose mortal taste brought death into the world, and all our woe."

WARNING

A double apricot kernel is said to be enough to kill a man. If eaten in excess, apricot fruit is believed to harm the bones and muscles, to promote blindness and falling hair, to numb mental facilities, and to injure parturient women.

FOLKLORE

Chinese almonds are the seed kernels of several sweet varieties of apricots used for almond cookies, eaten salted and blanched, or made into gruel or flour.

Afghans also use apricot seeds as almonds.

Ginger and licorice combined with sweet apricot kernels make a confection used as a cough suppressant and expectorant remedy.

Apricots are said to be a folk remedy for cancer.

A decoction of sweet apricot kernels made into a beverage is used for cough, asthma, and inflammations of the throat, nasal, and sinus passages. Kernel juice is used against hemorrhages.

After chewing sweet apricots, Tibetans apply them for eye disorders.

A paste obtained by crushing sweet apricot kernels is used for inflammation of the eyes.

In Korea, the expectorant sweet apricot kernel is used to treat dry throat.

In Chinese medicine, fruit of bitter almond is useful in heart disease.

Barley

Hordeum vulgare L.

"There is a boy here who has five barley loaves and two fish.
But what are they among so many people?"

John 6:9

POSIBLE BENEFITS

Diarrhea	*Poultices*
Gastritis	*Soothing ointments*

At the Sermon on the Mount barley loaves played a significant role in Jesus' "Miracle of the Loaves and Fishes." Jesus fed the multitudes with what the boy offered. He fulfilled the same miracle as the prophet Elisha in the Second Book of Kings. And Jesus did it with fewer loaves of barley and more people! I heard a new slant on the significance of this miracle just the other day. When everyone shares, there is enough for all to eat and not be hungry. What a concept! Share the bounty and no one has to leave the table hungry.

Barley was important to Israel throughout the biblical period. However, it was considered the food of the poor; the wealthy ate wheat. Barley played a major economic role in ancient Palestine as tribute.

Barley is able to survive heat and drought better than any other cereal grain, and it ripens in a shorter season that wheat. Barley has a lower protein content than wheat or rye, so the grain rarely was used alone in bread. Barley was mixed with millet, spelt, or pea meal. Barley is easily digestible and fed to convalescents. It is high in vitamins E, B6, B2, and folic and pantothenic acids.

The barley stalk was used as fodder for livestock. The seed was also used medicinally; barley water was prescribed as a soothing drink for parched throats and cooked barley as a poultice for sores and abrasions.

FOLKLORE

Malt syrup for beer was derived from barley (an important drink in ancient Egypt).

Necklaces made from barley seed have been found on mummies.

Among numerous other Egyptian medicinal uses, barley was used as a pregnancy test.

Bay Laurel

Laurus nobilis L.

I have seen the wicked in great power, and spreading himself like a green bay tree.

Psalm 37:35

POSSIBLE BENEFITS

Diabetes   *Insomnia*

Dyspepsia   *Migraine*

Earache   *Pain*

In Biblical times, the bay was symbolic of wealth and wickedness—usually the enemy's. In scripture, the bay laurel tree has been confused with the cedar of Lebanon and is sometimes cited as *daphne*, which is somewhat poisonous. The evergreen leaves of the bay, when broken, emit a sweet scent. Ancient Greeks and Romans twined the leaves into wreaths to crown their victorious athletes in the ancient Olympic games and equally successful soldiers returned from wars. The Roman gold coin of 342 BC has a laurel wreath modeled on its surface. King David was so taken with the power and beauty of bay laurel tree that he used the aromatic bay wood for paneling his personal rooms and the bay leaves in emblems and motifs to decorate the Temple.

Dried bay leaves are used to flavor meats, fish, poultry, vegetables, soups, and stews, and are especially popular in French dishes. They are an ingredient in pickling spices and vinegar. The leaves once were used as a tea substitute. An essential oil distilled from the leaves is used for flavoring food products, such as baked goods, confectionery, meats, sausages, canned soups, as well as in perfumery. The oil is preferred over the dried leaves because it can be measured more precisely, providing more uniform results.

Laurus nobilis L.

The fat derived from the fruits has been used for soap making and veterinary medicine.

King David was so taken with the power and beauty of bay laurel tree that he used the aromatic bay wood for paneling his personal rooms.

The leaves are twined into wreaths still, but they now crown, instead of sweaty and victorious brows, kitchen walls for culinary uses or a door with their aromatic and decorative beauty. The wood resembles walnut and can be used for cabinetry.

The essential oil pressed from the bay laurel's fruit has bactericidal and fungicidal properties. One story says that Emperor Nero had his apartments perfumed with the oil of bay leaf during epidemics to avoid being infected. An ointment or unguent de-

rived from the plant is said to remedy sclerosis of the spleen and liver and tumors of the uterus, spleen, testicles, liver, and stomach.

FOLKLORE

Bay leaves, when broken, emit a sweet scent and furnish an extract used by Asians in making perfumed oil. Bay leaf oil sometimes is used as a liniment or anodyne for earache.

Bay leaves and fruits, said to possess aromatic, stimulant, and narcotic properties, were once used for colic, cough, and hysteria. In small doses, leaves induce intense perspiration; in large doses, induce vomiting.

In Lebanon bay leaves and berries are extracted to relieve flatulence and act as a stomach tonic. Also, they tightly cork and steep the bay leaves and berries in brandy in the sun for several days. The residue, after subsequent distillation, is used as a liniment for rheumatism and sprains; the distillate acts to stimulate menstrual flow.

The Lebanese mountain people have used raw bay laurel berries to induce abortion. They macerate the berries in flour to poultice any dislocated joints.

The bay laurel fruit, prepared in various manners, is said to remedy facial growths or moles; fibrous tumors of the uterus and liver; hardening of soft tissue in the joints; and tumors of the eyes.

Black Cumin

Nigella sativa L.

For the fitches are not threshed with a threshing instrument, neither is a cart-wheel turned about upon cummin; but the fitches are beaten out with a staff, and the cummin with a rod.

Isaiah 28:27

POSSIBLE BENEFITS

Asthma	*Jaundice*
Bronchitis	*Tumors*
Colic	*Lactation*
Coughs	*Snakebite*
Fever	*Stomach aches*
Flu	

Black cumin has been translated as *fitches* and as *dill*. The black, pungent seeds are an ingredient for breads and cakes. Medicinally it purges the body of worms and parasites. According to an Arab proverb, "In the black seed is the medicine for every disease except death."

Black cumin is widely cultivated for its aromatic seeds, used whole or ground as a flavoring, especially in oriental cookery. Whole seeds are used in Russian rye bread and Turkish breads. Arabs mix the seed with honey as a confectionery. The tiny seeds are very hot to the palate, and are sprinkled on food like pepper; in fact, in Europe they are sometimes mixed with peppercorns.

Black cumin seeds may be used as a stabilizing agent for edible fats. A reddish-brown and semi-drying fatty oil is obtained from the seeds with benzene and subsequent steam distillation of the extract to remove about 31 percent of the volatile oil. Nigellone in the oil protects guinea pigs against histamine-induced bronchial spasms, suggesting the rationale behind its use in asthma, bronchitis, and coughs. The fatty portion of the extracted oil has been shown to increase breast milk in rats, verifying its folk usage for that purpose. In large quantities the seeds are also used to induce abortion. The seeds contain about 1.5 percent melanthine, a bad-smelling fish poison. The seeds have a folk reputation for treating abscesses and tumors of the abdomen, eyes, and liver; not surprising, since the seeds contain the antitumor sterol, beta-sitosterol.

According to an Arab proverb, "In the black seed is the medicine for every disease except death."

FOLKLORE

Black cumin seeds are strewn among woolens as a moth repellent.

Malayans poultice black cumin seeds onto abscesses, headaches, nasal ulcers, rheumatism, and inflammation of the testicles and penis.

Ethiopians add black cumin seeds to Capsicum pepper sauces and sprinkle them on bread and cakes.

Ethiopians mix black cumin seeds with melted butter, wrap them in a cloth, and sniff them for headaches.

Arabian women use black cumin seeds to increase lactation.

In Indonesia, black cumin seeds are added to astringent medicines for abdominal disorders.

Algerians take roasted black cumin seeds with butter for coughs, with honey for colic.

In Ayurvedic medicine, black cumin seeds are used as a purgative adjunct and are antiparasitic.

Lebanese take black cumin seed extract for liver ailments.

Black Mulberry

Morus nigra L.

They offered the elephants the juice of grapes and mulberries, to arouse them for battle.

1 Maccabees 6:34

POSSIBLE BENEFITS

Fever	*Sore throat*
Inflammation of the inner eyelid	*Painful menstruation*

It is a curious story from the First Book of Maccabees. Before going into battle against Judas, the Syrian king ordered that grapes and mulberry fruit be rubbed on the elephants' trunks to inflame them with anger. He was using the animals to force an opening in the ranks of the Israelites at Antioch. The reaction of the elephants may have been caused by the unripe mulberry fruit, which may cause hallucinations, nervous stimulation, and upset stomach.

The black mulberry tree is a native of Persia and was cultivated in some Grecian islands, Egypt, and Israel where it was known by the name *sycamore*. The fruit was eaten fresh or dried and its sweet juice was used to make wine. The fruit, resembling large blackberries, was preserved in brandy for desserts. The Greeks and Romans sometimes made mulberry wine or added the reddish-purple juice to color wine made from grapes. The root and bark were used as a laxative, and the bark provided tannin.

There are two mulberry species: black and white. The black mulberry tree is noted for its delicious fruit. It was likely imported into ancient Israel from Iran. The white mulberry came from China or India and was widely grown in Palestine and Syria as food for silkworms.

Morus nigra L.

The black mulberry is widely cultivated for its edible fruit, either eaten fresh or made into jams, jellies, sherbets, or wine. The fruits can be sun-dried and stored as a nutritious winter food. Black mulberry fruit should be picked very ripe, at its peak for

> *Before going into battle against Judas, the Syrian king ordered that grapes and mulberry fruit be rubbed on the elephants' trunks to inflame them with anger.*

sweetness and flavor. They are juicy and easily stain skin and clothes. To remove the stubborn black stains, rub skin and clothes with the juice from the unripe fruit. This is the principle behind removing red wine stains with white wine.

The black mulberry trees often are planted as ornamentals. The branches cascade to the ground, forming an umbrella of foliage. Wild birds, poultry, and hogs are fond of the fruits. Some farmers fatten their sheep with the berries, believing that they make the meat more digestible.

FOLKLORE

Europeans believe that the devil stains his shoes black with the mulberry fruit juice.

In Palestine they made a refreshing sherbet from sweet black mulberry juice and water infused with sweet-scented violet.

The Burmese worship the mulberry tree.

Iranians use the bark of the mulberry root to treat painful menstruation.

Medically, mulberry fruits are nutritious, fever reducing, and laxative. They're used to check thirst and to cool the blood.

Black mulberry fruit juice is boiled in honey for an ointment to treat throat tumors. A plaster made from the sap of black mulberry trees is used to remedy the hardening of soft tissue of the viscera.

A mixture of cow manure, crushed bilberry leaves, and olive oil is wrapped in fresh mulberry leaves and used to relieve earaches.

Cambodians use mulberry leaves to treat conjunctivitis.

Black Mustard

Brassica nigra L.

He said therefore, "What is the kingdom of God like? And to what should I compare it? It is like a mustard seed that someone took and sowed in the garden; it grew and became a tree, and the birds of the air made nests in its branches."

Luke 13:19

POSSIBLE BENEFITS

Appetite stimulant *Laxative*
Arthritis *Rheumatism*
Balm *Skin redness*
Diuretic *Stimulant*
Induce vomiting

This tiny, yet beneficial, herb is only mentioned in the parables of Jesus in the New Testament. In the Holy Land, this shrub grows to treelike proportions if there is no frost to kill back the growth. Mustard, first named by the Greeks, grew along the Sea of Galilee and has long been cultivated for mustard oil, a flavoring and a medicine.

Black mustard, cultivated for its seeds, is one source of commercial table mustard. The seeds contain both a fixed and an essential oil, used as a condiment, lubricant, and soap ingredient. Black mustard is mixed with white mustard to make mustard flour, then mixed with vinegar and water to produce various condiments such as English mustard. The leaves are eaten as a potherb. Mustard flowers are good necter producers for bees. In agriculture mustard is also used as a cover crop. Smoke from burning mustard is said to repel flies and mosquitoes.

As a medicine, black mustard is used in plasters, applied externally for many afflictions, like arthritis and rheumatism. A decoction or plaster of the seed can be applied in poultices for hardness of the liver and spleen.

Seeds are also said to help carcinoma and throat tumors. Recent research has shown that mustards contain five compounds that inhibit cancer due to exposure to tobacco smoke. However, mustard is a surface irritant that causes blood vessels to enlarge, causing loss of heat. Therefore, it is not used widely. It is this

---

Mustard, first named by the Greeks, grew along the Sea of Galilee and has long been cultivated for mustard oil, a flavoring and a medicine.

---

property of mustard that relieves congestion by drawing the blood to the surface when used for head afflictions, neuralgia, or spasms. Hot water poured on bruised seeds makes a stimulating foot bath, and the steam is good for colds and headaches.

FOLKLORE

Mustard is also recommended as an aperient ingredient of a tea useful in curing hiccups.

Black mustard oil is considered useful in treating pneumonia and abnormal conditions of the lung sac.

A gargle prepared from black mustard seeds is a folk remedy for throat tumors.

Mustard flour is considered antiseptic.

Old herbals suggested mustard for baldness, epilepsy, snakebite, and toothache.

Ayurvedics value the black mustard leaves for throat complaints and worms, the seeds for coughs and skin ailments.

Mustard oil is said to stimulate hair growth.

Bottle Gourd

Lagenaria siceraria Molina

The cedar within the house had carvings of gourds and open flowers;
all was cedar, no stone was seen.

1 Kings 6:18

POSSIBLE BENEFITS

Alzheimer's Disease	Headaches
Baldness	

The gourds alluded to in the Bible are exclusively African. Specimens that have been found in Egyptian tombs dating from 3500 to 3000 BC. According to biblical literature the bottle gourd or calabash was not used for food but as a container for liquids.

In the Book of Joshua the town of Dilean, mentioned as belonging to one of the tribes of Judah, is probably derived from *delaath*, a term occurring in post-biblical literature for the bottle gourd or calabash.

The wild gourd mentioned in the Bible was practically inedible as a mature plant. Gourds and squash are best eaten when young and tender.

The wild gourd mentioned in the Bible was practically inedible as a mature plant. Gourds and squash are best eaten when young and tender. As a food, it can be bitter—perhaps mildly toxic like its relative the zucchini—or insipid like so many of the related pumpkins and squashes. Members of the squash or pumpkin genus were unknown in

---

Members of the squash or pumpkin family were unknown in Europe and the Middle East until after the discovery of America.

Europe and the Middle East until after the discovery of America. However, it's astonishing to note that gourds similar to the calabash have been discovered in Peru, dated about 7000 BC.

Bottle gourd contains high quantities of choline, the lack of which is associated with infertility (fenugreek is another high choline plant). Low incidence of choline in the brain chemistry has been linked to higher incidence of Alzheimer's disease. Like many food plants, bottle gourd may have a wealth of medicinal applications that have yet to be fully explored.

FOLKLORE

In the Celebes, natives collect their palm juice for making palm wines in the calabash or bottle gourd.

In India and Nigeria a decoction of bottle gourd leaves is given for jaundice. The seed is taken internally or the seed oil applied externally for headache. Under some conditions, the fruits may be purgative, if not poisonous. It is even on record that sailors who drank their beer from gourds became ill.

On the Malay Peninsula, bottle gourd

leaves are used to treat baldness. The gourds contain sitosterol, the major ingredient in saw-palmetto lipid extracts used in treating baldness and BPH.

Malayans eat the fruit of the bottle gourd to treat colic with fever. The juice of young fruits has been used locally to

quench the thirst of patients with typhoid. Mixed with lime juice, bottle gourd is used as an astringent to treat pimples.

Bottle gourds are used to make musical instruments in Borneo and hats in the Philippines.

Butcher's Broom

Ruscus aculeatus L.

But he himself went a day's journey into the wilderness, and came and sat down under a solitary broom tree. He asked that he might die: "It is enough; now, O LORD, take away my life, for I am no better than my ancestors." Then he lay down under the broom tree and fell asleep. Suddenly an angel touched him and said to him, "Get up and eat."

1 Kings 19:4–5

POSSIBLE BENEFITS

Difficulty in breathing

Fever

Inflammation due to exposure to the cold

Jaundice

Kidney Infection

Painful urination

Broom grows principally in deserts, hills, and rocky areas of Israel. It is often the only source of shade, as Elijah discovered. Butcher's broom grows wild, and sometimes it is cultivated as a spiny ornamental hedge. The roots were used for charcoal.

Ruscogenin has been isolated from the broom and is identical with Sapogenin B, used as a starter material for steroids. Maude Grieve in her book *A Modern Herbal* suggests that the young shoots of butcher's broom have often been prepared and eaten like the stalks of asparagus. For millennia the mature branches were bound up and sold as brooms.

FOLKLORE

In Lebanon, the butcher's broom rhizome is sliced and dried and decocted for nose, throat and sinus infections as

Ruscus aculeatus L.

well as to alleviate copious urination, water retention, jaundice, kidney trouble, and respiratory difficulties.

The butcher's broom root, considered a very mild laxative, increases perspiration and relieves water retention. It is also suggested for tubercular tumors, urinary obstructions, and kidney infections.

A decoction of butcher's broom, sweetened with honey, is an expectorant that can relieve labored breathing.

An infusion of butcher's broom treats high fevers.

Capers

Capparis spinosa L.

Also when they shall be afraid of that which is high, and fears shall be in the way,
and the almond tree shall flourish, and the grasshopper shall be a burden,
and desire shall fail: because man goeth to his long home, and
the mourners go about the streets.

Ecclesiastes 12:5

POSSIBLE BENEFITS

Arthritis   Fractures
Cancer   Malaria
Cataracts   Sciatica
Dysentery

In Ecclesiastes "desire shall fail" refers to capers. The ancient Israelis served capers as an appetizer and named the flower buds "desire shall fail" because eating capers abates hunger until the main course is ready to eat.

Capers are pickled flower buds in your spice cabinet. Commercial capers are harvested from the wild or from cultivated

The wood is said to be termite resistant. The juice of the plant is said to be antibactericidal and fungicidal.

shrubs in Mediterranean climates. They are steeped in vinegar or some other preservative. For pickling, one kilo of buds is steeped in one kilo of brine vinegar for a month. Sprouts, buds, and young shoots of the plant are sometimes eaten like asparagus. The wood is said to be termite resistant. The juice of the plant is said to be antibactericidal and fungicidal. Leaves and ripe fruits are grazed by goats and sheep.

FOLKLORE

Europeans in the tropical zones often bruise the caper leaves as poultices for gout. Root and bark, soaked in wine or vinegar, are applied internally or externally for hardening of soft tissue (bladder, kidney, liver, spleen, uterus), tumors (head, groin, liver, neck), and warts.

In India, the caper fruits are crushed and the juice poured into the ear for earache.

In Greece, Cream of Capers™ is a

cosmetic that preserves the skin in good color with few blemishes.

The Spanish believe that eating capers holds off old age.

The Ormara Indians make a jelly from the capers to apply for rheumatism and snakebite.

In parts of India, capers are used against pulmonary tuberculosis and for treating burns, sores, and wounds.

North Africans use capers to ward off arteriosclerosis, chills, and eye diseases.

Bedouins inhale steam from boiling caper root bark for headaches. They grind the leaves to make an overnight poultice to relieve arthritis pain.

Iranians use the caper plant to treat malaria, rheumatism, and fever.

Lebanese regard the caper roots as treatment for both malaria and reducing spleen enlargement following malaria. They boil the roots for dengue fever, malaria, and Malta fever.

Carob

Ceratonia siliqua L.

And he would fain have filled his belly with the husks that
the swine did not eat; and no man gave unto him.

Luke 15:16

POSSIBLE BENEFITS

Asthma   High cholesterol
Cancer   Hoarseness
Cough

In the story of the Prodigal Son, the younger son asked for his inheritance early and spent it quickly and riotously. When he had no money left, he hired himself out as a swine tender. Because he had no money for food, he longed to eat the carob pods fed to the swine.

In the Bible the pods of carob seeds are called St. John's bread or locusts. John the Baptist lived rough and ate what he could gather. The carob pods, or locusts, were primarily used as animal fodder, although in times of famine humans also ate them. When ripe the pods are sweet.

The seeds of the carob were used as an ancient standard weight throughout the Mediterranean. Goldsmiths used carob seeds to balance the scales and weigh precious metals. The Greek word *carat* means "fruit of the carob."

Once upon a time, according to Maude Grieve in *A Modern Herbal*, the seeds were in demand by singers because they cleared the voice. There is more truth than fiction in this belief; research has verified that potions made from the plant are effective against coughs and relieve respiratory tract disorders. Carob seeds work against inflammations in the air passages in the throat and head, soothe throat irritations, and promote healing. Carob pods also contain the anti-tumor compound gallic acid that confirms its folk reputation for fighting cancer.

Carob trees are cultivated for their fruit and seeds, which are both high in sugar and calcium and low in protein and fats. One tree can

---

Carob seeds work against inflammations in the air passages in the throat and head, soothe throat irritations, and promote healing.

---

produce 800 pounds of husks. In health food stores carob is sold as a chocolate substitute. Anyone for a 24-carob-coated walnut?

FOLKLORE

In southern Europe, carob pods are used for asthma and coughs.

Carob is also used in textile printing, synthetic resins, insecticides, and fungicides.

In Cyprus a brittle candy known as pasteli is made from carob pods.

In Palestine, a molasses named dibs is prepared from ripe carob fruits.

American imports of carob pods are mostly used in tobacco flavorings and cosmetics.

Alcoholic beverages have been
made from infusions of the carob pod.

Roasted carob seeds have been used as a
coffee substitute.

Castor bean

Ricinus communis L.

And the Lord God prepared a gourd,
and made it to come up over Jonah,
that it might be a shadow over his head.

Jonah 4:6

POSSIBLE BENEFITS

AIDS   *Laxative*
Emollient

POISON

Seed capsules

Biblical text refers several times to gourds, either gourd vines or shrubs. The castor bean gourd is a tree that thrives in arid desert conditions. It grows rapidly, and its large, spreading leaves provide shade from the scorching hot days, as Jonah discovered under his gourd tree.

Castor beans, or castor-oil beans, are cultivated for their seeds. They yield a fast-drying, non-yellowing oil, used mainly in industry and the preparations of various medicines. Egyptians used the oil in lamps 6,000 years ago. They also used it as poultices for headaches and blended it with fats to stimulate luxurious hair growth. The oil was also a base for unguents to treat eye disorders, fungi, and constipation.

Castor oil has excellent absorption qualities. Be careful what ingredients you mix with it because the additives will be quickly absorbed into the body. Currently, the pale-gold oil is used in cosmetics. Its rich, spreadable, fast-drying, non-sticky texture makes it useful in lipsticks, nail polish, cream blushes, skin moisturizers, and sunscreens. It rarely causes skin irritation. Fatty acids make the castor bean oil soothing to the skin, and

Egyptians used the oil in lamps 6,000 years ago. They also used it as poultices for headaches and blended it with fats to stimulate luxurious hair growth.

hydroxyl acid gives the castor bean oil its characteristically high viscosity. Castor bean oil is a major ingredient in a cosmetic skin-firming lotion with witch hazel lotion, corn oil, wheat germ oil, glycerin, and retinyl palmitate. It is one of the ingredients in Oil of Olay™.

Castor bean oil has been used as an all-purpose lubricant in manufacturing from coating fabrics and other protective coverings to greasing the conveyors that carry food and aircraft hydraulics. The oil is non-sticky and transparent. It's used to dye and preserve leather. Rilson, a polyamide nylon-type fiber, is produced from castor bean oil. Dehydrated castor bean oil is an excellent drying agent used in paints and varnishes, waxes, polishes, carbon paper, candles, and crayons.

Ricin, a toxic protein in castor bean seeds, acts as a blood coagulant, but it has other applications as well. Ricin can be attached to monoclonal antibodies that attack only cancer cells, a technique reportedly tried in 1,000 cancer patients. Ricin may play another role in the treatment of AIDS. The AIDS virus can infect an immune cell by locking onto its cell receptor protein CD4. By genetically affixing ricin to genetically engineered CD4 proteins, the reengineered CD4-ricin will lock onto the external viruses of infected cells one-thousand times more often than on healthy cells. Techniques like this may possibly kill enough infected cells to prevent the disease from spreading within the body and causing the life-threatening AIDS symptoms.

Castor bean oil has been used as an all-purpose lubricant in manufacturing from coating fabrics and other protective coverings to greasing the conveyors that carry food and aircraft hydraulics.

Castor oil is a purgative and has labor-inducing properties. Ricinoleic acid is used in contraceptive jellies. Castor bean oil is used externally for dermatitis and eye ailments. Seeds also contain the alkaloids ricinine and toxalbumin ricin, which are considered purgatives and are counterirritants to scorpion stings and fish poison.

I wish my mother had read the warning label: "Not to be administered to children under 12 years of age." I might still like orange juice. My mother assumed that castor oil, cut with orange juice, was a panacea for all childhood ailments. Today she could have been arrested for child abuse.

WARNING

Castor bean seeds are poisonous; the oil is pressed from the seed. Small seeds are richer in oil than large seeds.

FOLKLORE

Food grade castor bean oil is used as an antistick agent in candy, to coat medicinal tablets, and as a flavor component (butter and nut) in baked goods, beverages, candies, desserts, and meat products.

Castor bean oil and seed have been used as folk remedies for warts, tumors, corns, and moles.

Castor bean leaves are applied to the head to relieve headaches; as a poultice they are applied to boils.

Castor beans and castor oil are a dangerous ingredient in folk remedies.

Chicory

Cichorium intybus L.

They shall eat lamb that same night; they shall eat it roasted over the fire with unleavened bread and bitter herbs.

Exodus 12:8

POSSIBLE BENEFITS

AIDS	*Impotence*
Asthma	*Insomnia*
Cancer	*Menstruation*
Diabetes	*Rapid, irregular heartbeat*

Chicory may be one of the bitter herbs of Passover; we'll never really know just what they did eat. Just as in biblical times, people of the region still gather and eat chicory leaves with lamb and unleavened, or yeast-free, breads. The leaves are considered suitable for consumption, but they can be tough and bitter. When they are blanched or parboiled, they lose their bitterness and the "greens" have a pleasant taste. Preparing herbs like this may not be kosher for Jews celebrating Passover. The bitterness is to help them remember their enslavement in Egypt. The sweetness signifies the rejoicing of their deliverance.

Whole or shredded chicory leaves are served with oil and vinegar in salads. The blanched hearts can be prepared as a raw or cooked vegetable. The new shoots of young plants make reasonable animal fodder, but older plants may embitter animal milk. Root-chicory, established in Europe during the Napoleonic blockade, is cultivated as a coffee substitute. French and Cajun immigrants brought their chicory-flavored coffee to New Orleans. When blended with ground coffee, ground chicory roots enhance the flavor and aroma of the brew. Chicory has almost three times more tinctorial power than coffee. Roots are used in seasoning soups, sauces, and gravies, and to impart a rich deep color.

Chicory is also the namesake of cichoric acid, which may help in the battle against AIDS because of its antiviral activity and its ability to boost the immune system.

Carolus Linnaeus, the famous Swedish botanist, used chicory in his floral clock because of its regularity of opening and closing (5:00 AM to 10:00 AM in Sweden, 6:30 AM to noon in Britain, and 8:30 AM to 12:30 PM eastern daylight time in the United States). The pretty blue flowers can also be eaten fresh or pickled in salads.

Chicory coffees or liqueurs might better be recommended than caffeinated alternatives for heart patients. Chicory tinctures might be of value in controlling arrhythmia, fibrillation, or rapid, irregular heartbeats. Caffeine can exacerbate these conditions; chicory acts to calm them.

Chicory is also the namesake of cichoric acid, which may help in the battle against AIDS because of its antiviral activity and its ability to boost the immune system. Cichoric acid and its closely related compounds—along with those of dandelion, endive, and milk thistle—may be useful in treating osteoarthritis by retarding the degradation of collagen. A combination of chicory, hops, and peppermint has been documented to relieve the pain of chronic inflammation of the gallbladder. Perhaps we should reclassify chicory as one of the "better" herbs.

FOLKLORE

Some Lebanese peasants consider fresh chicory leaves eaten as a salad cleansing and restorative; the juice from macerated leaves is sedative and soothing; the root is calmative and believed to overcome the stimulus of coffee.

Like its fellow bitter herb dandelion, chicory has a folk reputation as a cure or preventive of liver problems.

Iroquois use the chicory roots to wash or poultice chancres and fever blisters.

In Central America, chicory is regarded as a diuretic, an expectorant, and a laxative. It is also used for asthma, bilious fevers, and jaundice.

Europeans use chicory for chronic inflammation of the stomach lining and piles.

Chicory flowers are reportedly tick-repellent, and the latex-like sap fungicidal. The roots are being

investigated for antimalarial activity.

Cherokee Indians use the chicory roots as a tonic for the nerves.

Chicory is said to protect the liver from the excesses of coffee-drinking.

Powdered chicory seeds are applied for inflammation of the spleen.

Chicory leaf, boiled with honey, is used as a gargle for cancer of the mouth.

Ukrainians use the chicory plant for disorders of the small intestine and stomach and, with other herbs, for bronchitis, inflammation of the nasal

and sinus passages, diarrhea, hemorrhoids, toothache, worms, and wounds.

Chicory was regarded as an aphrodisiac,
and its seeds were used in love potions.

Homeopathically, chicory is used for
gallbladder and liver ailments.

Recent research has found that crude
ethanolic extract of chicory seeds administered orally one to ten days after sex exhibited significant contraceptive activity.

In Iran, chicory, like endive, is used
as a cooling medicine in attacks of excess
bile.

Chicory leaf is used as a potherb and an
ingredient in seasoning.

Chicory leaf has been used as a sedative
and laxative, while the dried root has
been used as a diuretic and tonic.

Cinnamon

Cinnamomum verum J. Presl

I have perfumed my bed with myrrh, aloes, and cinnamon.

Proverbs 7:17–18

POSSIBLE BENEFITS

Bronchitis	*Herpes*
Candida	*Pain*
Diabetes	*Painful menstruation*
Dyspepsia	*Rheumatism*
Fever	*Tuberculosis*
Heartburn	

The clever woman in Proverbs ensnared her young man by decorating her room with tapestry, carvings, and fine linen from Egypt and perfuming them with aloes, cinnamon, and myrrh. The cinnamon plant was imported from India and Sri Lanka to Egypt and the Holy Lands via Phoenician ships and Arabian caravans. In biblical times, cinnamon was more that a spice; it was used to prepare incense and holy oils for religious rites, medicine, and perfumes. According to Exodus 30:22–25, the translation reads that cinnamon was an ingredient in the holy oil that God ordered Moses to use in the Tabernacle to anoint both the sacred vessels and the officiating priests. Cinnamon leaves, like laurel leaves, were woven into decorative wreaths in Roman temples.

Cinnamon has been used medicinally for thousands of years. Ancient Chinese used it as early as 2700 BC. The Egyptians used cinnamon in ancient embalming mixtures. In the 12th century, Hildegard of Bingen recommended it as "the universal spice for sinuses" and to treat colds, flu, cancer, and "inner decay and slime." The latter certainly covers anything missed by the former.

Cinnamon, obtained from the inner bark, is dried in the shape of quills or cinnamon

Cinnamomum verum J. Presl

sticks. Today we primarily use cinnamon as a flavoring spice. Hot apple cider, toast, cookies, candies, and fruit salads seem to

Cinnamon has been used medicinally for thousands of years. Ancient Chinese used it as early as 2700 BC. The Egyptians used cinnamon in ancient embalming mixtures

improve with a dash of cinnamon powder. Try steeping a quill of cinnamon in a glass of cranberry juice. Cinnamon can soothe the stomach, possibly preventing ulcers. Modern science has shown what the ancients,

herbalists, and Hildegard knew all along: cinnamon can prevent infection and indigestion, as well as a host of other bodily ailments, including fever, diarrhea, and menstrual problems. Cinnamon contains the antitumor agent benzaldehyde. Its antiseptic properties help kill the bacteria that cause tooth decay and gum disease. It kills disease-causing fungi and viruses and might even head off urinary tract infections and the fungus responsible for vaginal yeast infections (Candida).

More importantly, it may help diabetes. In Type II, or non-insulin-dependent diabetes, the pancreas produces insulin, but the body cannot use it efficiently to break down glucose, the simple sugar that fuels body functions. The USDA researchers discovered that cinnamon reduces the amount of insulin necessary for glucose metabolism. In other words, this herb may help metabolize sugar for diabetics whose bodies have trouble doing so. One-eighth of a teaspoon of cinnamon was shown to triple insulin efficiency, according to the USDA research.

WARNING

In its powdered form, culinary amounts of cinnamon are nontoxic, although allergic

> *(C)innamon can prevent infection and indigestion, as well as a host of other bodily ailments, including fever, diarrhea, and menstrual problems.*

reactions are possible. Cinnamon oil distilled from the leaves is a powerful germicide; however, applied directly to the skin, it may cause redness and burning. Taken internally, it can cause nausea, vomiting, and possibly even kidney damage. Do not consume straight cinnamon oil.

FOLKLORE

The Portuguese made candles from the fat gathered from boiling the fruit of the cinnamon tree.

Expectant mothers are given hot cinnamon tea with ginger and caraway to prevent blood clotting.

Lebanese use cinnamon as a stimulant to relieve colds, rheumatism, and halitosis, as well as to check slobbering in young and elderly people.

Ayurvedics consider cinnamon bark an aphrodisiac and tonic. They use the oil for belching or vomiting, flatulence, loss of appetite, and nausea.

Cinnamon is used to stimulate the uterine muscles to reduce excessive bleeding during menstruation and during tedious labor to correct defective uterine contractions.

Cinnamon has been regarded as a folk remedy for cancer (especially of the rectum, breast, gums, mouth, stomach, and uterus), hardening of soft tissue (especially of spleen, breast, uterus, liver, and stomach), and tumors (especially of the abdomen, liver, and sinews).

Citron

Citrus medica L.

And you shall take on the first day the fruit of goodly trees.

Leviticus 23:40

POSSIBLE BENEFITS

Asthma *Lumbago*

Bronchitis *Seasickness*

Dyspepsia

The goodly tree was valued for its aromatic flowers and fruit. Citron—*etrog* or *ethrog* in Hebrew—was used in the Jewish Feast of Tabernacles or Sukkot. Four plants are presented to Temple in symbolic remembrance of the Hebrews' agricultural past: citron, palm, myrtle, and willow. The ceremony requires that the citron fruit is relatively mature, fresh, clean, without defects, and symmetrical. It must come from a tree that hasn't been grafted but grown from cuttings or seedlings. The citron and pomegranate along with the menorah are the traditional symbols of Judaism.

Citron has a very thick peel that enables it to last a long time on the tree or when picked. Over the centuries agriculturists have adapted the citron so it has more pulp, more juice, and a thin rind, to be sold as lemons. The fruits are used to flavor meat and to perfume the breath. Citron husk is produced as candied peel by soaking the rind in brine and preserving it in sugar. It is an essential ingredient in cakes and confections.

Citron may be *another* candidate as the forbidden fruit from the "tree of knowledge" in Genesis in addition to the apple, apricot, orange, pomegranate, and fig. According to Winifred Walker in *All the Plants of the Bible*, the English herbalist Gerard refers to the citron as the "Assyrian apple tree." The citron is also referred to as *pomum adami* (which means Adam's apple).

*The goodly tree was valued for its aromatic flowers and fruit. Citron—*etrog or ethrog *in Hebrew—was used in the Jewish Feast of Tabernacles or Sukkot.*

FOLKLORE

The Chinese prescribe citron rind as an aromatic digestive. They use a decoction of the fresh shoots as a very mild laxative, a digestive aid, and a dewormer. They prepare the root as an expectorant and for lumbago.

The Indochinese dice the citron fruit into alcohol and prescribe it for asthma.

Malayans make a poultice of citron leaves to relieve arthritis and headaches.

Citron was used to prevent seasickness and pulmonary and intestinal disorders.

The juice, bark, and rind of citron are used in folk remedies for cancers and tumors.

The preserved citron rind is a suggested remedy for dysentery.

The Spanish use citron syrup as an expectorant in cough medicines.

Citron wood is white, fairly hard,

fine-grained, and rather heavy; it is used in making agricultural implements.

Citron juice reduces fevers and is an astringent.

Oil of citron is extracted from the root and peel in Italy and Sicily.

Citron peel and pulp are ingredients in marmalade and other preserves and jams.

Branches from the citron tree are used as walking-canes in Puerto Rico.

The Japanese and Chinese use citron to perfume rooms and clothing and as moth repellent.

Like flowers of other citrus species, citron blossoms are an important source of honey for bees.

Coriander

Coriandrum sativum L.

The house of Israel called it manna; it was like coriander seed, white, and the taste of it was like wafers made with honey.

Exodus 16:31

POSSIBLE BENEFITS

Acid indigestion	*Neuralgia*
Heartburn	*Rheumatism*
Halitosis	*Toothache*
Impotence	

It is difficult to reconcile the white flakes of the heavenly manna with the brown seeds of coriander. We now know that manna and coriander are two different things. Perhaps Coriander's white flowers are the source of the confusion. Coriander grows quite well in Egypt and Israel; I have seen it in both places.

The coriander seeds are the size of a peppercorn and have a sharp, though pleasant, aroma. The young plants are known as cilantro or Chinese parsley and are used in

The plant was used as early as 1550 BC for culinary and medicinal purposes. It was one of the drugs employed by Hippocrates around 400 BC.

85

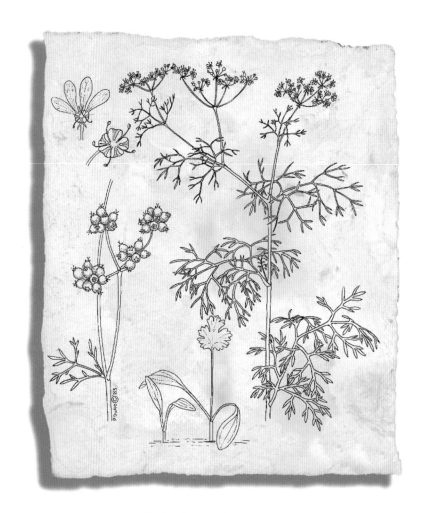

Coriandrum sativum L.

salads as a vegetable as well as in chutneys, sauces, and soups. Coriander is an important ingredient in curry. All parts of the plant have a strong odor. The seeds are used for flavoring food and beverages and give perfumes a wood-

> *Coriander is cultivated primarily as a spice and drug source. Dried fruits, called coriander seed, are fragrant, combining the taste of lemon peel and sage.*

land fragrance. Coriander is cultivated primarily as a spice and drug source. Dried fruits, called coriander seed, are fragrant, combining the taste of lemon peel and sage. Whole seeds

are sometimes coated with sugar for a confection or used to flavor gin or vermouth.

Medicinally, coriander seeds were prescribed as a stimulant and antiflatuant. If eaten in excess, they have the harmful effect of a narcotic. The plant was used as early as 1550 BC for culinary and medicinal purposes. It was one of the drugs employed by Hippocrates around 400 BC. My research tells me that cilantro might help in chelating various minerals in the body. Some researchers think that cilantro might help neutralize mercury or iodine, but more research is needed. Like licorice, coriander contains twenty chemicals with antibacterial action that can control body odor. The essential oil of coriander helps soothe indigestion and eases gas.

FOLKLORE

Like many carrot-related spices, coriander contains coumarins that often have blood-thinning properties.

Coriander is a Cantonese folk remedy for bad breath. Boil a few ounces of fresh leaves in two cups of water for a few minutes, then drink it or use it as a mouthwash.

Ethiopians chew the leaves to relieve colic and stomachaches.

The Lebanese use coriander as a spice and narcotic as well as an antiflatuant and stimulant.

In Ethiopia, coriander leaves are added as an aromatic to bread, spiced sauces, and tea.

A decoction of coriander seeds is taken as a medical stimulant; in excess, it acts as a narcotic analgesic.

The Unani consider coriander seed an aphrodisiac and a tonic to the brain, heart, and liver.

Confectioners in Europe add coriander to baked cakes and sweetmeats.

Arabs find it a wholesome spice, as do the Egyptians and Indians, who add it to their meat.

Extracted coriander seed cake is used as fodder.

A plaster or unguent made from coriander juice is said to remedy hot tumors.

In the Philippines, the leaves are eaten raw with native dishes and used to flavor soups.

Pills made from coriander seed are folk remedies for abdominal tumors.

Ayurvedics recommend coriander for dysentery.

Coriander was used in love potions and as an aphrodisiac mentioned in *The Thousand and One Nights*.

Iranians smoke coriander fruits for toothaches and chew the leaf for headaches.

Cucumber

Cucumis sativus L.

And daughter Zion is left like a booth in a vineyard, like a shelter in a cucumber field, like a besieged city.

Isaiah 1:8

POSSIBLE BENEFITS

Diuretic   *Windburn*
Skin irritations

Cucumbers are 99 percent water. Egyptians could not have contemplated life without cucumbers. In the heat of Africa and the Middle East they made a refreshing meal. They were so important that the cucumber fields were protected by guardposts to keep out wild animals and thieves as was the custom for vineyards and olive orchards. In Isaiah Israel is left unprotected, with no one watching at the guardposts.

Cucumbers are most famous as a vegetable. They are less famous as a soup ingredient or as cosmetics, but no less important.

In fact, the Lebanese make a favorite salad of cucumbers and yogurt; they also use the salad to soften skin, dispel acne, smooth rashes, and heal sunburn. Slices of cucumber relieve swollen and irritated eyes. Cucumber soap and lotion are especially beneficial for windburn and relieve other superficial irritations. Cucumber juice is said to kill cockroaches and repel fish moths and wood lice. Strewing green cucumber peels on the floor at night was supposed to be effective against insects.

FOLKLORE

In Korea, cucumber salve is used for burns, scalds, and skin disorders. The juice from the leaf is used as children's

Cucumis sativus L.

emetic. A decoction of the roots is a treatment for beriberi.

In Ayurvedic and Unani medicine cucumbers are used like melons. The fruit is regarded as cooling and diuretic.

Cucumber soup has been prescribed to relieve urine retention.

The Lebanese believe that eating cucumbers prevents colds. They mix the sap

that oozes from the scraped cucumber peel with yogurt to treat cold sores.

In Indochina, candied cucumber is prescribed to children to relieve dysentery. The fruit or its juice treats gallstones.

Iranians use cucumber seeds for typhoid.

Malayans eat young cucumber leaves raw or steamed.

Cumin

Cuminum cyminum L.

When they have leveled its surface, do they not scatter dill, sow cummin, and plant wheat in rows and barley in its proper place, and spelt as the border?

Isaiah 28:25

POSSIBLE BENEFITS

Abnormal heart rhythm	*Dysentery*
Asthma	*Fainting spells*
Dermatitis	*Impotence*

Note: In quotations from the Bible, the word is spelled *cummin*. Today's dictionary spells it *cumin*.

God conducts his business according to plan, and He instructs His people to farm according to plan so they can feed themselves and be prosperous.

The spice cumin is used today much as it was in biblical times; it is crushed and ground, mixed with bread or added to meat, fish, and stews. Egyptian cooks sprinkled the seeds on bread and cakes. Cumin seeds have been found in an Egyptian grave of the 18th Dynasty, but not in archaeological excavations in Israel. Cumin is a powerful aromatic seed, similar to caraway but larger.

Today the seeds flavor breads, cheeses, chutney, meat, pickles, rice, sauerkraut, sausage, and soups. The essential oil expressed from the seeds is used in liqueurs and perfumes. Mediterranean people speak of "cummin splitters," or avaricious individuals, greedier than our "hair splitters." Indigenous to Turkey and Egypt, cumin now grows throughout the Mediterranean region.

The essential oil was used medicinally as a disinfectant. Oil of cumin is bactericidal and larvicidal. Cumin also has antioxidant properties, and the oil is somewhat anesthetic. In

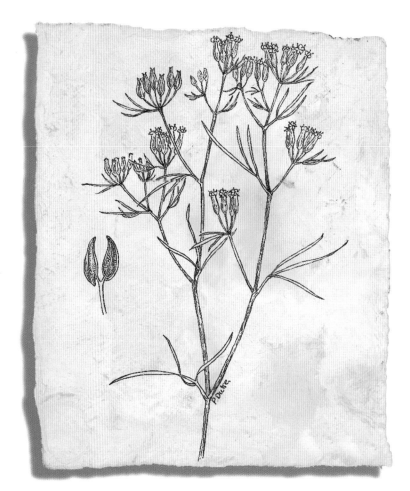

Cuminum cyyminum L.

biblical times, cumin was used as a medicine and an appetite stimulant. Also, it is considered to be antispasmodic, astringent, and antiflatuant. My research shows that the spice

---

The essential oil was used medicinally as a disinfectant. Oil of cumin is bactericidal and larvicidal.

---

contains three pain-relieving compounds, seven anti-inflammatory properties, and four that combat sweating. If I had carpal tunnel syndrome, I would add lots of cumin to my curried rice and other spicy dishes.

FOLKLORE

Ayurvedics list the following among cumin's virtues: an aphrodisiac and a poison antidote; they also use it for belching, excess bile, intestinal worms, consumption, dysentery, eye diseases, fever, leprosy, scorpion stings, and tumors.

In ancient Assyria, cumin with garlic was prescribed for constipation and gas.

Lebanese use cumin seed oil, sometimes with orange flower water, for cramps, fainting, and rapid heart rate.

The Unani use the fruit of cumin to treat asthma, boils, sties, gonorrhea, hiccups, inflammations, and ulcers.

Arabs consider oil of cumin as aphrodisiac, mixed with honey and pimento and taken three times a day.

North Africans place a poultice of cumin on the nape of the neck for mumps.

Ethiopians apply pounded cumin leaves to skin disorders.

In Iran cumin seeds are prescribed for the pain that often follows childbirth.

Dandelion

Taraxacum officinale Weber

In the second month on the fourteenth day, at twilight, they shall keep it;
they shall eat it with unleavened bread and bitter herbs.

Numbers 9:11

POSSIBLE BENEFITS

Cancer	*Osteoporosis*
Diabetes	*Rheumatism*
Hepatitis	*Sciatica*

The children of Israel probably learned to eat bitter herbs from the Egyptians. Ancient Egyptians used to place the green herbs on the table, mix them with mustard, then dunk their bread in the mixture. Dandelion may be one of several candidates for the bitter herb of Passover, including chicory, lettuce, endive, watercress, and sorrel. The feast of Passover lasts seven days, the first and last days being most solemn. It is celebrated by Jews in memory of their ancestors who had to flee in haste from Egypt.

Dandelion (native to Europe, not the Middle East) gets its name from the French *dent de lion*, referring to the pointed edges of the leaves resembling the "tooth of a lion." Dandelion is sometimes eaten raw in salads, but often it is blanched like endive and used as a green, frequently cooked with salt pork or bacon to enhance the flavor. Roots are sometimes pickled. The flowers are used to make a wine. Ground, roasted roots are used for dandelion coffee and sometimes mixed with real coffee. Dried dandelion leaves are an ingredient in many digestive or diet drinks and herb beers. Birds like the seeds, and pigs devour the whole plant. Goats eat the leaves, but sheep, cattle, and horses do not care for it. Dandelion has also been used as a source of latex.

Dandelion leaves are a rich source of

97

Taraxacum officinale Weber

vitamin C and have a higher content of beta-carotene than carrots. Dandelion roots, considered a diuretic and mild purgative, have long been used for chronic disorders of the kidney

---

Dandelion may be one of several candidates for the bitter herb of Passover, including chicory, lettuce, endive, watercress, and sorrel.

---

and liver. Most diuretic drugs have the unfortunate side effect of depleting the body of vital potassium, which can aggravate cardiovascular problems. As well as being a natural diuretic, dandelion is one of the best sources of natural potassium.

Dandelion roots have been used to treat jaundice, a yellowing of the skin generally associated with a malfunctioning liver. The flowers are well endowed with lecithin, a nutrient that is effective against various liver ailments. I suggest steaming the roots, leaves, and flowers as a "green" way to protect and heal your liver. Other possible benefits of dandelion include:

- young shoots trail behind cabbage in being high in boron and calcium;

- leaves contain silicon that can help strengthen bones; and

- stems of newly opened flowers contain a compound that stimulates the pancreas to produce insulin (they must be eaten fresh).

The next time you weed and feed your lawn, let the dandelions battle the blue grass. In fact, don't use any weed-and-feed poison; the dandelions may take over the blue grass free of charge.

FOLKLORE

Europeans settlers introduced the dandelion to the American Midwest as food for bees.

Kiowa women used a decoction of dandelion leaves for menstrual cramps.

Chippewa take an infusion of dandelion root to induce the flow of breast milk after childbirth.

Native Americans made a yellow dye from boiled dandelion flowers and roots.

They also made a leaf tea as a general tonic and a root tea for heartburn.

Cherokee use dandelion for toothaches and as a blood medicine and sedative.

Dandelion extracts are found in anti-smoking compounds in modern times.

Date Palm

Phoenix dactylifera L.

On the first day you are to take choice fruit from the trees, and palm fronds, leafy branches and poplars, and rejoice before the Lord your God for seven days.

Leviticus 23:40

POSSIBLE BENEFITS

Asthma	*Gonorrhea*
Cough	*Toothache*
Fever	*Tuberculosis*
Estrogen deficiency	

The best known reference to palms is that of Jesus' entry into Jerusalem, where he was welcomed and acclaimed "King of the Jews." Spreading, carrying, and waving palm branches was a sign of respect long used by Jews to indicate celebration and triumph in their Feast of Tabernacles, or Sukkot. Sukkot was a harvest festival held upon tithing the first harvest to the Temple. According to Leviticus, four species of plants were offered: fruit from the goodly tree or citron tree, branches of palm, boughs of myrtle, and willows of the brook.

The food value of the date palm included fresh and dried fruit and honey. Fruits were preserved by drying or pressing into large cakes. A date syrup, or "honey," was pressed from the fresh fruit. Honey from bees is mentioned only four times in the Bible, while date "honey" is mentioned forty-nine times. Dates are loaded with iron and potassium but low in protein and fats. Many Arabs supplement a diet of dates with some form of milk. In both ancient and modern times, nomadic peoples have eaten a diet consisting only of dates and some sort of dairy for months at a time—roaming ancient Israel on milk and honey.

The life-giving properties of the palm and

its survival in the barren deserts has been a symbol of strength and longevity throughout history. Palm fronds were symbols of Judea; after the Romans forced Judea into retreat, the palm replaced the bay laurel leaves as the Roman symbol of victory. After centuries of persecution, Christians adopted the palm as a sign of triumph over *both* the Hebrews and the Romans. During those times the palm became a symbol of martyrs, the triumph of faith over the destruction of the body. Its Latin name, *Phoenix*, is translated from Phoenicia (modern Lebanon and Syria), "the land of the palms."

From earliest times the date palm was associated with Palestine. It was the symbol on its coinage. To those who inhabited Palestine, the illustration suggested the straight and erect growth of the tree, its unbranched and unencumbered stem, and the beauteous crown of leaves at its summit. It would also remind them that the palm flourished in the desert; its presence always indicated moisture. The Arabs have a saying about the palm tree: "Its head should be in fire (sunshine) and its feet in water."

Another adage is, "There are as many uses for dates as there are days in the year." Date palm leaves are woven into mats. The midribs are used for fencing and roofing. The fibers provide thread and rigging for boats. Wood from the palm trunk is cut into planks and used for doors, beams, and rafters. Flour is

---

The life-giving properties of the palm and its survival in the barren deserts has been a symbol of strength and longevity throughout history.

---

derived from the pith of the tree. The heart of palm is eaten in salads. Oil expressed from the seeds is used to make soap. The kernels are ground up or soaked in water for days and used for animal food. In medieval days, the palm was thought to prevent sunstroke, avert lightening, cure fevers, and drive away mice and fleas. The sap of the palm tree, collected in the morning, ferments by evening. This may be one of the strong drinks mentioned in the Bible, or it may be the date honey that the ancient Israelites fermented into date honey wine. The Hausa of East Africa still add dates with hot peppers to native beer to make it less intoxicating.

Two superstitions about how powerful dates are may have scientific support for

In medieval days, the palm was thought to prevent sunstroke, avert lightening, cure fevers, and drive away mice and fleas.

the folk tales. One goes, "The pollen of the male date palm mixed with water is a charm against childlessness." Egyptians believe, "To swallow three date stones will prevent

childbearing for many years." Both date pollen and date seeds, parts of the palm that are not normally consumed, contain estrogen hormones that affect female fertility cycles.

FOLKLORE

Unripe date fruits are used as an astringent for hemorrhoids by the Arabs.

In the Holy Land, large date palm leaves are still used to cover the roofs and sides of houses and to solidify reed fences.

Nigerians feed dates with bran to immature young heifers to make them more prolific.

North Africans use dates, with other ingredients, in vaginal suppositories to enhance fertility.

The Lebanese believe the sugar from dates helps hepatitis. They apply powdered seeds to any affliction.

Algerians smoke the date palm seed powder to reduce fevers.

Desert Date

Balanites aegyptiaca (L.) Delile

Is there no balm in Gilead, is there no physician there?

Jeremiah 8:22

POSSIBLE BENEFITS

Antiseptic	*Herpes*
Burns	*Malaria*
Cough	*Rheumatism*
Colic	*Syphilis*

The Monks of Jericho regard the desert date as the balm of the Bible. They prepare an oily gum from the fruit that is sold in tin cases to travelers as the balm of Gilead. (At least seventeen plant species have been suggested as the balms in the Bible.) The juice left over from drying dates is called "date honey" and was used to treat chest complaints.

The date wood is used to make axes, cudgels, Islamic writing boards, mortars and pestles, walking sticks, and wooden bowls.

Since it gives off little smoke when burned, it is a favorite firewood for burning in covered places. Spiny branches are used to make pens for animals. The bark yields a strong rope fiber. The fruit is fermented to make an intoxicating beverage. In West Africa and Chad the seed is used for making breadstuffs and

Desert date oil, which constitutes 40 percent of the fruit is both eaten and used to make soap

Balanites aegyptiaca (L.) Delile

soups, the whole leaf is used as a vegetable, and the pericarp crushed and eaten. Desert date flowers are eaten in soups in West Africa.

Desert date oil, which constitutes 40 percent of the fruit, is both eaten and used to make soap. North Africans use the fruit as a detergent. The fruits are pounded and boiled to extract the medicinal vulnerary oil. The oil is poured over open wounds and apparently acts as an antiseptic. It forms a protective covering against secondary infections. One Turkish surgeon regards the oil as one of the best digestive aids as well as a most excellent remedy for curing wounds.

FOLKLORE

Extracts of desert date root have proven slightly effective in experimental malaria treatment. The bark has been used in treating syphilis.

Ethiopians use desert date bark as an antiseptic, the leaf to dress wounds, and the fruit as a deworming laxative.

The Ghanaians use the stem of desert date fruit in fumigation to heal the wounds of circumcision. They use the leaves as a dewormer.

The desert date bark contains the toxin saponin that is lethal to fish, mollusks, and tadpoles.

Nigerians consider that desert dates can induce abortions.

Libyans use desert date leaves to clean malignant wounds. They use powdered root bark for herpes zoster while the root extracts treat malaria.

In Chad the desert date is used to treat

liver disease, the seed to reduce fevers, and the fruit for colds.

fruit to aching bones and swollen rheumatic joints.

Ugandans use desert date oil to treat sleeping sickness, but this medicinal application has never been verified.

Ayurvedics apply desert date fruit oil to skin ulcers and use the fruit to treat other skin ailments and rat bites.

Lebanese apply the oil from desert date

Dill

Anethum graveolens L.

*For dill is not threshed with a threshing sledge, Nor is the
cartwheel driven over cummin; but dill is beaten out with a rod,
and cummin with a club.*

Isaiah 27:27

POSSIBLE BENEFITS

Cancer	*Dyspepsia*
Colic	*Estrogen deficiency*

Dill, anise, caraway, and black cumin seeds sometimes are difficult to distinguish from each other in biblical text, depending on the writer or translator. Dill and cumin seeds are so tiny they would be lost or destroyed if the proper tools weren't used to harvest and winnow the crop. The Talmud records that dill seeds, stems, and leaves were subject to being tithed. The whole plant was valued for its culinary and medicinal mainstays: dill seed, dill leaves and stems called *dill weed*, and essential oil of dill. The good farmer could not afford to lose his crop through wasteful harvesting methods.

Dill was grown by the ancient Greeks and Romans and used as a kitchen herb. The dill seed was used as a food flavoring, a condiment, an aromatic, and a breath freshener. Medicinally, dill was prescribed to relieve the pressure and pain associated with flatulence. Dill water made from a decoction of the seed and containing dill oil was recommended for gastric and intestinal upsets.

Dried fruits (seeds) are used in pickles, soups, spiced beets, fish, and fish sauces, with eggs and in potato salads. Roasted fruits have served as a coffee substitute. Hot extracts of the fruit are used to make jams

Anethum graveolens L.

and liqueurs, and the dill oil is used in other liqueurs. Fresh leaves are used in salads, with cottage cheese, cream cheese, steaks, chops, avocado, cauliflower, green beans, squash, tomatoes, tomato soup, zucchini and shrimp. Dried leaves are also used to season various

---

Dill was grown by the ancient Greeks and Romans and used as a kitchen herb. The dill seed was used as a food flavoring, a condiment, an aromatic, and a breath freshener.

---

foods. Oil from dill seed is used chiefly as a scent in soaps and perfumes and in the pickle industry. Dill weed oil, from the above-ground parts of the plant, is used in the food industry because of its characteristic dill herb smell and flavor.

Cooking causes dill weed to lose its delicate aromatic flavor, so it is always added to foods just before they are ready to be served. Drying the dill weed does the same. However, the ripe seeds retain their flavor after being dried.

Like fennel, aniseed, and coriander, dill makes a "warming" tea that soothes the stomach and intestines and relieves cold symptoms and upper respiratory infections. Dill seed oil is antibacterial, showing inhibitory effects on various organisms, like Bacillus anthracis.

Dill contains several important phytochemicals: anethole and myristicin are insecticidal. However, anethole can cause dermatitis. Dianethole and photoanethole appear to enhance estrogen levels; bergapten (5-methoxypsoralen) has been shown effective in psoriasis and skin discoloration. Eugenol is a recognized anesthetic, anodyne, antiseptic, bactericide, and insecticide. Scopoletin is a uterine relaxant.

FOLKLORE

Ayurvedics use dill seed to relieve

abdominal pain, bilious attacks, eye ailments, fevers, ulcers, and uterine pains.

Dill is a folk remedy for cancerous conditions.

Ethiopians use dill to remedy gonorrhea and stomachaches and to ease the pain of childbirth. The dill leaves are boiled in coffee or tea or chewed as a diuretic and a laxative. They use the fruit for coughs and headaches. Ethiopians use tender plant parts, dried fruits, and flowers in flavorings, especially alcoholic beverages.

In Lebanon, dill tea is used interchangeably or together with Pimpinella for colic in babies. Drops of dill oil are taken for dyspepsia, and sometimes the oil is mixed with charcoal, starch, and gums like acacia or tragacanth to make a digestive pill.

Fava bean

Vicia faba L.

Take wheat and barley, beans and lentils, millet and spelt; put them in a container and make bread for yourself.

POSSIBLE BENEFITS

Alcoholism	*Impotence*
Cancer	*Parkinson's disease*
Estrogen deficiency	*Pneumonia*

CAUTION

Allergic reactions	*Toxins*

The fava bean, a likely candidate for the bean in scripture, is among the first vegetables harvested in the spring. References to the fava or broad bean appear in Pliny's journals but are not prominent in the Bible. Perhaps, at the time the Book of Ezekiel was written, beans were not popular among the elite class. The fava bean was believed to cause nightmares and insanity. Fava beans also had a reputation for causing improper behavior: flatulence.

Since biblical times the beans have been dried, ground into flour, mixed with wheat or barley, and baked into breads. In Egypt they were, and still are, made into breadstuffs. Today, as in biblical days, fava beans are cultivated as a vegetable, green or dried, fresh or canned. Broad beans have been used as a meat extender or even a meat substitute, as well as a skim-milk substitute. Sometimes fava beans are grown for stock feed; the beans are fed to horses and the stalks are given to camels.

Some people credit China's ginseng consumption for its large population, but China is also the world's biggest producer of fava

Vicia faba L.

Broad Bean Sprouts-in-a-Jar

(From The Complete Sprouting Cookbook by Karen Cross Whyte,
published by Troubadour Press, 1973)

*Soak whole, undamaged beans overnight in lukewarm water: 4 cups water to 1 cup
beans will make four cups of sprouts.*

*The next morning, rinse the beans thoroughly, drain off all excess water, and put
them in a big jar.*

*Cover the top of the jar with cheesecloth, nylon, screening, or anything clean that lets
air in; secure with a rubber band; and lay the jar on its side.*

*Rinse the beans three or four times a day (you can do this through the screen),
draining thoroughly each time.*

Keep out of direct sun; keep at 70 to 80 degrees F with good air circulation.

In three to five days, your beans will sprout. You can now give them a
little sun if you want to "green them up." Start eating when the sprouts are
about 2 inches high. (Start a new batch once the current batch is ready to eat
so you won't run out.) Use in salads or sandwiches. Remember, these sprouts
are likely to be ten times as phytochemically potent as cooked beans; just an
ounce or two a day would provide potential benefits for most people.

beans. Fava beans have a noteworthy folk reputation as an aphrodisiac. Research now confirms that fava beans contain significant quantities of L-dopa, the biological precursor of the catecholamine dopamine. Was Cicero anticipating the male arousal effects of L-dopa

---

The fava bean might be better for the prevention of breast and prostate cancers than the currently heralded drug Tamoxifen.

---

when he accused the beans of the Bible of inflaming the passions? In ancient Greece, fava beans were fed to athletes to improve their performance, perhaps foreshadowing our Olympic anabolic steroid problems.

Seers, prophets, and oracles of those days avoided the bean, believing ingestion clouded their vision and dimmed their foresight. Even Hippocrates (460–377 BC) believed the bean injurious to the vision. Today the *Physician's Desk Reference* lists double and blurred vision, dilated pupils, and nightmares as some of L-dopa's drawbacks. How correctly our ancestors anticipated the side effects of this natural drug! Small wonder they often avoided the bean. Nonetheless, poorer people of the world, then and now, eat the beans, boiled or roasted like peanuts, and even make breadlike patties out of fava bean flour or meal.

It is interesting that those who live in the Mediterranean countries and consume vast quantities of fava beans are also the greatest at-risk population to their toxicity, especially from the roasted fava nuts. Because of an inherited enzyme deficiency among Greeks, Italians, and Semitic peoples, their consumption of roasted fava beans can cause hemorrhage, even death. It is ironic that this vegetable, which offers so many health benefits, can be deadly.

Research studies today confirm the good health/bad health duality of the fava bean and its phytochemical constituents. Two of the most powerful chemicals found in fava beans are dopamine from natural L-dopa and genistein. Certain varieties of fava bean possess remarkably high levels of natural L-dopa, which has been used successfully in antiaging therapy. Fava beans have a much better fat-to-protein ratio than soy beans and may *possibly* contain even more anti-breast cancer compounds (specifically, Bowman Birk inhibitors,

---

Since biblical times the beans were dried, ground into flour, mixed with wheat or barley, and baked into breads.

---

estrogenic isoflavones, phytic acid, phytosterols, and saponins) than soy. The fava bean might be better for the prevention of breast and prostate cancers than the currently heralded drug Tamoxifen. In addition to having the highest naturally-occurring L-dopa content of any plant, fava beans are also rich in genistein, a natural estrogen that has shown great potential against breast cancer. It prob-

ably even protects against the embolisms that Tamoxifen is known to cause.

Stems of the fava bean contain daidzein, which modulates increases of dopamine, and can successfully treat alcoholism and other habit-forming addictions including cocaine, morphine, and nicotine addictions. The L-dopa in fava beans increases levels of dopamine in the brain. Increasing dopamine may quell cravings for alcohol and other addictive drugs that tend to "reward" the brain with dopamine. In that sense, fava beans might even help with depression. In Parkinson's disease, there is an imbalance between dopamine and acetylcholine in the brain, usually due to degeneration of the dopamine-producing cells in the brain. L-dopa naturally increases the level of dopamine activity in the brain. When the brain is no longer able to generate dopamine naturally, fava beans can take over and do what the body cannot do for itself.

A popular Roman legend related that the spirits were said to flee anxiously when they caught scent of fava beans. Sound familiar? Enzyme-based products like Beano™ make all dried beans easier to digest, greatly reducing or eliminating the gases that cause discomfort and embarrassment. Another method of reducing flatulent-causing gases is to rinse and soak the beans. Rinse dry beans well, and let them sit in fresh water for several hours. Rinse them again and let them soak, preferably overnight. The same goes for canned beans: rinse and soak them. They will retain all of their desirable characteristics while losing much of their singularly undesirable one.

A Chinese study showed the L-dopa levels in fava bean sprouts to be ten times greater than those of the dry beans from which they were sprouted. Fava bean sprouts are much richer in *some* anticancer compounds than dried beans and are not a health risk, unless the sprouts develop bacteria contamination, warns the USDA.

WARNING

L-dopa is a hard drug with many side effects. It should be used only on the advice of a physician or health care professional. Like many beans, fava beans can cause allergies. Many people, especially of Mediterranean origin, are allergic to fava beans, an allergy which is potentially fatal. Anyone trying any new food for the first time or anyone consuming large amounts of any food for protective or medicinal purposes should tell their health care provider what they are doing. Be cautious.

FOLKLORE

North Africans take two grilled fava beans in the morning for stomach distress; they also use them for liver and kidney disorders.

Roasted fava bean seeds are eaten like peanuts in India.

In ancient times fava beans were used in voting: a white bean signified approval and a black one condemnation. Magistrates were elected by casting beans.

In Iran, young fava bean shoots are said to be efficacious in rousing a drunkard from his stupor.

Fenugreek

Trigonella foenum-graecum L.

We remember the fish we used to eat in Egypt for nothing, the cucumbers, the melons,
the leeks, the onions, and the garlic, but now our strength is dried up, and
there is nothing at all but this manna to look at.

Numbers 11:5–6

POSSIBLE BENEFITS

Baldness	*Milky vaginal discharge*
Diabetes	*Pain*
Dyspepsia	*Rheumatism*
High cholesterol	*Swelling*

I'm not sure how far along the Israelites were in their forty-year flight from Egypt, but at this point in the Numbers story they were tired of manna and bitter herbs. They craved meat. And they began to wonder if life back in Egypt had been really all that bad. There they had lamb, and fish they could get for nothing. And in the desert the thought of juicy watermelons and cucumbers and succulent leeks and garlic could

drive them mad. They were ready to mutiny. Upon their return to the Promised Land, they never forgot their desert hardship. They celebrated the Passover feast, and they planted fenugreek immediately.

Some scholars consider the fenugreek a more likely translation of the Hebrew *hasir* (literally meaning "herbs") to be the leeks of the Bible. Fenugreek also has wide use in the Middle and Near East today; in Lebanon the seeds are a snack, as popular as the peanut is in America. The Lebanese even make a "milkshake" popular in the treatment of hypertension; just soak the fenugreek seeds to make a drink of the green mush.

Fenugreek seeds have been found at Tell Halaf in Egypt, and an Iron Age sample was

Trigonella foenum-graecum L.

found at Lachish in Israel. Fenugreek has always been the food of the poor in the Near East; it was regarded as the food of humility.

Fenugreek seeds have been used for millennia as a general cure-all for "whatever ails you" from Egypt to India, and most likely all around the Mediterranean. Fenugreek seeds were an important ingredient in Lydia Pinkham's compound. (Because of its 18 percent alcohol content, Lydia's elixir should hardly have been prescribed for high blood sugar.) However, the bittersweet seeds of fenugreek contain at least five compounds reported to help diabetics lower blood sugar. In laboratory tests, the seeds have been shown to delay the transfer of glucose from the stomach to the blood, thus reducing the amount of insulin needed to maintain healthy blood sugar levels.

Lydia Pinkham's Vegetable Compound

12 ounces fenugreek seed

8 ounces unicorn root (Aletnis)

6 ounces life root (Senecio)

6 ounces black cohosh (Cimicifuga)

6 ounces pleurisy root (Asclepias)

Add enough alcohol to make 100 pints (6 gallons) of the compound. (You may want to make a smaller batch.)

FOLKLORE

The fenugreek leaf has been used medicinally as a disinfectant.

In India, fenugreek seeds are used as a condiment and in perfumery.

Europeans add fenugreek seeds to hay, especially old hay, to make it more appealing to animals.

The Lebanese also claim that a steady diet of fenugreek speeds the healing of broken bones and helps patients recover from chest inflammations and typhoid.

West Africans use fenugreek seeds as a source of a yellow dye. They also substitute them for coffee.

At a Lebanese clinic, patients reported using fenugreek seeds as a poultice and for diabetes, dyspepsia, fever, and heart trouble.

Unbelievable but true, one side effect of consuming fenugreek sprouts is that it may increase a woman's bust size. Anise, caraway, fennel, lemongrass, and fenugreek may increase the size of breasts and promote lactation, while parsley, mint, and sage may reduce a woman's milk supply.

Figs

Ficus carica L.

[B]ut they shall all sit under their own vines and under their own fig trees, and no one shall make them afraid; for the mouth of the Lord of hosts has spoken.

Micah 4:4

POSSIBLE BENEFITS

Cancer	*Thrush*
Ringworm	*Wound healing*
Skin discoloration, scarring	

In biblical imagery the fig tree symbolizes prosperity and peace. It just doesn't get much better than to be able to sit under your own grape vine and fig tree in your own yard, especially after having beaten those swords into plowshares. The fig tree is the first fruit tree mentioned in the Bible: Adam and Eve sewed fig leaves together to cover their shame and nakedness. Some suggest that the fig was the forbidden fruit of the Garden of Eden. In Deuteronomy figs are among the seven plants that God promised the Hebrews when they reached the Promised Land: wheat, barley, grapes or vine, figs, honey or date palm, olive

Medicinally, figs may hold the cures for cancer, AIDS, and diabetes.

trees, and pomegranates.

Fig fruit, fresh or dried, was made into cakes and wine. Threading cakes or figs on strings made them portable for travel. "Cakes of

123

Ficus carica L.

Figs" are mentioned in the First Book of Samuel. The Assyrians used dried figs as a sweetener. The leaves were woven into baskets, dishes, and umbrellas. Medicinally, the fruit proved an effective laxative and tonic; it was used as well in poultices to treat infections, tumors, or boils. King Hezekiah was dying from a malignant swelling. The prophet Isaiah pounded the fruit into pulp for a poultice and applied it to the tumor, thus healing Hezekiah's malignancy. We now know that figs contain psoralen, an antidote to Staphylococcus.

To the ancient Egyptians the fig represented the Tree of Life. Throughout the Middle East figs are still a staple food. Figs are consumed fresh, dried, preserved, candied, or canned. They are used as desserts and jams and in pastries, confections, and fruitcakes. Lower grades of dried figs are used for the production of alcohol and wine in Mediterranean countries, while better grades are sold commercially in fancy packs. Fig Coffee™, a coffee substitute, is manufactured in Europe. Spiced or pickled figs, fig bread, fig meat, and fig brownies are considered delicacies. Fig leaves, gathered after the fruits have ripened, are used as animal fodder.

Medicinally, figs may hold the cures for cancer, AIDS, and diabetes. In 1998 Serraclara

and associates found that a decoction of fig leaf taken with meals for a month lowered insulin doses for Type 1 diabetics by 12 percent. An active ingredient in figs, benzaldehyde, has been effective in experiments on mice afflicted with Ehrlich carcinoma. It has been used to treat cancers of the gums, neck, liver, uterus, and testicles. Dried figs might be a useful dietary source of boron, reported to double blood levels of sex hormones and to prevent

Corn/Wart Removal Remedy

Open a fresh fig.

Tape the pulp to the corn or wart overnight (use plastic sheets if necessary).

Remove the fig the next morning and soak your foot in hot water.

Remove the corn or wart.

In stubborn cases, repeat overnight treatments three to five times. Or use an ancient removal remedy: apply the white latex milk that oozes from fig twigs or leaves once a day for between five and seven days.

If that doesn't work, sit under your grape vine, put up your feet, and peel back a fig to eat and enjoy.

osteoporosis. The antitoxin psoralens derived from fig leaves may be instrumental in experimental treatments for AIDS. Medical science already uses psoralens to treat blood diseases and psoriasis.

Like papaya and pineapple, figs contain protein-dissolving enzymes that help get rid of unwanted skin growths, including corns and warts.

One final note on figs for those descendants of Adam and Eve; fig leaves are still sewn together, but now they are used as wrappings for fresh fruit.

FOLKLORE

North Africans rub the painful inflammation of the inner eyelid with fig leaves, then bathe it in a rose water infusion of almonds.

Chinese apply fig leaves to hemorrhoids. Ficus rennet, which coagulates animal milk and milk-like preparations from vegetable seeds, may be used for the preparation of cheese and junkets and in medicine.

Tropical Americans used figs for washing pots and pans. Fig juice was even an ingredient in some household detergents, but was abandoned when users developed skin disorders.

Africans use the fresh fig root in a lotion for thrush.

In France an essential oil named Fig Leaf Absolute™ is used in perfumery for woodland scents.

The latex from figs, containing the proteolytic enzyme ficin, is used in many of the applications for which papain is employed.

Green or unripe figs are said to be poisonous; the poison is replaced by sugar when the fruit ripens.

also believe that eating the dried fruits facilitates conception.

Africans drop the latex from figs in ant holes to drive away the ants. Africans

Ayurvedics use figs for nosebleeds, leprosy, and diseases of the blood and head.

Flax

Linum usitatissimum L.

The priest shall put on his linen vestments after putting on his linen undergarments next to his body; and he shall take up the ashes to which the fire has reduced the burnt offering on the altar, and place them beside the altar.

Leviticus 6:10

POSSIBLE BENEFITS

Arthritis   *Heart disease*

Bronchitis   *Inflammations*

Cancer   *Rheumatism*

Dermatitis

Only the finest cloth was suitable for wear or use in the Temple. Israelite priests wore linen garments, and tables were spread with linen cloth. Linen has always been considered among the finest cloths. Linen breathes and is absorbent; it allows air to circulate and soaks up and retains moisture, making the body cooler and dryer. If that isn't enough, linen is anti-allergic and filters out the burning rays of the sun. The wrinkles show that linen is doing its "thing," a small price to pay for comfort.

Linen is one of the world's oldest textiles; the earliest fragment of cloth ever identified (considered to be of linen) was from Eastern Turkey, carbon dated to 9,000 years ago. Ancient Egyptians depicted the growth of flax, the spinning of flax thread, and the weaving of that thread into linen on papyri and in murals. Mummified remains of the Pharaohs are bound in fine and delicate linen, woven with an expertise that is still difficult to replicate today, 3,000 to 4,000 years later. Linen also was used to make mummy cases, and flaxseed oil was used in the embalming process.

Flax was grown extensively in Egypt, and linen is the most important product made

Linum usitatissimum L.

from the flax fiber. Linen fibers are prepared by retting and scrunching the stems; the stems are soaked in water to separate the tough fibers and soft tissue. After combing, the fibers are spun. Flax fibers are soft, lustrous, and flexible, although not as flexible or elastic as those of cotton or wool. Linen is more durable than silk and three times stronger than cotton. Linen is stronger wet than dry, which made it popular for sails and wing coverings in early airplanes. The fiber from the stalks was used in thread, curtains, wicks for lamps, mummy wrappings, and masks, cartonnage (paper made from linen and papyrus).

The words *linen, lining, linear, liniment,* and *lineage* all derive from the word *line* from a Latin or Greek root *linum,* meaning "flax." Even the plumb line used in construction may have a biblical origin. The world of art owes much to this "line" of thought. The finest artist's canvases are made of linen, and linseed oil is often used as a vehicle for the pigments in painting. One of the first mechanically reproduced Bibles printed by Johannes Gutenberg used the "pigment" lampblack, and the drying agent was predominantly boiled linseed oil. Early rugs made of flax were replaced in 1860 with linoleum (linum = "flax"; oleum = oil) floor covering.

The seed produces linseed oil, edible when cold pressed. Medicinally, the seeds were prescribed as a demulcent, emollient, and laxative; flaxseed was also used as a remedy for burns. I have been trying to convince the FDA that flaxseed is and has been a food for mil-

---

Medicinally, the seeds were prescribed as a demulcent, emollient, and laxative; flaxseed was also used as a remedy for burns.

---

lennia. The three principal components of nutritional significance are alpha-linolenic acid (ALA), dietary fiber, and polyphenolics (particularly lignans). The ALA slows blood clotting; prevents inflammation and relieves colitis, arthritis, and gastritis, among others; retards and prevents tumor growth; and boosts the immune system. The lignans in flaxseed are particularly useful in preventing breast and colon cancers.

Folklore

Linseed oil mixed with equal quantities of lime water, or Carron Oil, is an excellent application for burns and scalds.

Crushed flaxseeds make a good poultice for colds and pleurisy.

Ayurvedics use flax leaves for asthma

and coughs, the seeds for backache, bilious attacks, consumption, inflammation, leprosy, ulcers, and urinary discharges.

In Ethiopia flaxseeds are used to treat amoebic dysentery.

A poultice made from hot flaxseeds is applied to abscesses and swellings from rheumatism.

Frankincense

Boswellia sacra Flueck.

When they saw that the star had stopped, they were overwhelmed with joy.
On entering the house, they saw the child with Mary his mother; and
they knelt down and paid him homage. Then, opening their treasure chests,
they offered him gifts of gold, frankincense, and myrrh.

Matthew 2:10–11

POSSIBLE BENEFITS

Dysentery	*Gonorrhea*
Fever	*Polyps*

The magi brought the newborn Jesus three gifts: gold to recognize his kingship; frankincense to acknowledge his holiness or divinity; and myrrh to symbolize the hardship and suffering that he would endure.

Frankincense is an important ingredient of incense. Literally, *frank* means "free" and *incense* means "lighting." The Arabic word for frankincense, *luban*, means "milk of the Arabs." The aromatic gum, obtained by means of incisions in the stem, was used for incense, perfume, holy ointments, and as a fumigant. It was imported by caravan from Arabia and East Africa; the plant did not grow in Israel. Frankincense was highly esteemed by the Egyptians for embalming and fumigating.

Incisions are cut into the bark of the frankincense shrub. The milky juice that exudes hardens into "tears" within a few weeks. These tears are collected. They are favored in Lebanon primarily as incense and secondarily as a medicine or cosmetic. Today, frankincense is still used as incense in Roman Catholic churches. Essential oil of frankincense, or oil of olibanum, is used in high-grade perfumes, especially for oriental and floral types. Several modern perfumes contain frankincense, including Mennen Millionaire, Sculptura by Jovan, and Volcan d'Amour by Diane von Furstenburg.

FOLKLORE

Pliny mentioned the resin from frankincense as an antidote for poison hemlock.

Speakers of Swahili use the resin from frankincense as a diuretic.

In Tanzania the resin from frankincense is boiled in sesame oil and taken for schistosomiasis, a parasitic disease. They also make a decoction from frankincense resin with cinnamon and cardamom to relieve stomachaches.

Recent authorities maintain that the incense used in the Tabernacle was a mixture of frankincense, galbanum, onycha, and stacte. The use of any incense not composed of these four ingredients nor in the proper proportions was strictly forbidden.

East Africans use the resin from frankincense to treating syphilis.

Asian Indians use the resin from frankincense for rheumatism and disorders of the nervous system.

A dose of thirty-five grains of frankincense is said to improve the memory.

Inhaling vapors from frankincense is said to alleviate bronchitis and laryngitis. The bark resin is used as a tonic and a diuretic in East Africa.

The Chinese use frankincense for uro-genital ailments.

Frankincense is used in Asia for leprosy and rheumatism.

Frankincense has been suggested as a mosquito repellent.

Garlic

Allium sativum L.

["] We remember the fish we used to eat in Egypt for nothing, the cucumbers, the melons, the leeks, the onions, and the garlic; but now our strength is dried up, and there is nothing at all but this manna to look at."

Numbers 11:5–6

POSSIBLE BENEFITS

Angina	*Flu*
Cancer	*Hypertension*
Colds	*High cholestrol*
Diabetes	*Infections*

No wonder the strength and spirits of the Hebrews following Moses out of Egypt and through the desert were flagging. They needed garlic, leeks, and onions to give them strength and stamina. An inscription on one Egyptian pyramid reads that 100,000 men were employed for thirty years in its construction. The laborers were fed garlic, leeks (fenugreek), and onions as part of their stipend. And the ancient Israelites had forty years of struggling through the desert to the promised land without even one clove of garlic!

Hebrews have relied on garlic to be able to "be fruitful and multiply" as Genesis directed. They have believed consuming garlic increases virility. According to the Talmud, there are five properties of garlic consumed on Fridays (Shabbat).

It keeps the body warm.

It brightens the face.

It increases semen.

It kills parasites.

It fosters love and removes jealousy.

Allium sativum L.

Why Fridays? After the women's ritual Friday bath, or *mikvah*, the men could have sex with their wives, with their consent. And the use of garlic to increase virility is not just

Medicinally, garlic juice was prescribed to treat intestinal infections, respiratory ailments, snakebites, melancholy, and hypochondria

an interesting bit of folklore or ritual. Garlic has a high content of free amino acids dominated by the amino acid arginine. Arginine is used by the cells that line the artery walls to manufacture nitric oxide, which facilitates blood flow to the penis. Without nitric oxide, erections are impossible.

Since earliest times garlic has been culti-vated in Egypt and the Near East for its pungent bulb. It was a staple food in Egypt, grown as a vegetable on a large scale. Garlic was consumed fresh, dried, or powdered as a seasoning. It continues to be one of the most popular vegetables in the Mediterranean countries today.

Medicinally, garlic juice was prescribed to treat intestinal infections, respiratory ailments, snakebites, melancholy, and hypochondria. Today, medical research has identified the phytochemicals that support many "old wives' tales." For example, garlic contains the active ingredient ajoene, reported to inhibit platelet aggregation in arteries. Garlic juice contains allicin, an antibiotic and antifungal element shown to have antitumor properties. From around the world, folk remedies include inhaling vapors from the garlic stalk, ap-plying a poultice made from the bulb, or mas-saging with an ointment made from garlic roots to relieve headaches, reduce tumors, and provide antifungal and antibacterial relief.

Garlic's anticancer and antitumor repu-tation is no less stellar. Allicin, a powerful antibiotic, has been isolated as the "silver bullet" that protects the body from carcino-gens and bacteria and facilitates healing, lowers blood sugar, alleviates hypertension, and speeds healing from gunshot wounds. If spinach gave Popeye the strength of ten men, garlic gave 100,000 pyramid builders their strength for thirty years.

Remember, the next time you ask your friends to help you paint your house or put in a flagstone patio, feed them lots and lots of garlic; hold the beer until the project is finished.

FOLKLORE

Hippocrates prescribed eating garlic to cure uterine tumors.

Garlic juice mixed with oil is useful for curing skin diseases, ulcers, wounds, and insect bites. This same mixture can be used as drops for earaches.

According to an ancient manuscript in India (ca. AD 450), garlic was prescribed for abdominal tumors.

Garlic has antibacterial properties that make it a useful expectorant in the treatment of tuberculosis.

Garlic acts as pain relief for headaches, earaches, and rheumatic pains.

Grape (Vine)

Vitis vinifera L.

I am the true vine and my Father is the gardener. He cuts off every branch in me that bears no fruit, while every branch that does bear fruit he trims clean so that it will be even more fruitful.

John 15:1–2

POSSIBLE BENEFITS

Arthritis	*Hypertension*
Heart disease	*Rheumatism*
Herpes	*Tuberculosis*

Grapevines are the first cultivated plant mentioned in Genesis. The vine became the symbol for Israel, according to the Books of Jeremiah, Ezekiel, and Hosea. In the New Testament, Jesus declared, "I am the true vine and my Father is the gardener." In the first Book of Kings and Micah, the vine represented peace and prosperity. When Noah stepped off the ark, he planted a vineyard. He also embarrassed himself by getting quite drunk from the fruit of that vine. Noah could have taken a little advice that the Talmud offers women in dealing with this potent sexual stimulant.

One cup of wine is becoming to a woman.
Two cups are degrading.
And if she has three, she solicits publicly.
If she has four, she solicits even an ass in the streets and cares not.

Recent research does show that women tend to get drunk faster on less alcohol than men and take longer to recover from the effects of overdrinking. Could the writers of the Talmud have been onto something?

Vitis vinifera L.

Vinegar was not a condiment in ancient Israel; poor or sour wine (vinegar) was the wine ration given to Roman soldiers. It was thought to strengthen the blood, make the soldiers fierce and strong in battle, and prevent diarrhea. The Roman soldiers certainly were

---

Red wine's ellagic acid

may help prevent cancer.

---

reputed to be formidable warriors. I wonder if having to drink vinegar made them bad-tempered as well.

Wine was used as an anesthetic and to reduce the anguish of capital punishment. When Jesus was dying on the cross, he refused to drink from the sponge soaked in vinegar because he had to fulfill his fate and suffer unto his very death.

The vine was probably the first Bible plant to be cultivated on a large scale. It was grown by Romans in France and in southern Europe. In biblical times, the vines were usually grown in vineyards situated on slopes. They were generally surrounded by stone walls to keep out wild animals and thieves. There were also stone towers between the walls to guard over the vineyards. At first vines were grown so that they crept over rocks and walls. Only later were they trained and cultivated as bushes. They were often grown over porches so that you could sit under your vine in the shade at the hottest time of the day.

Resveratrol, a stress metabolite present in grape leaves and grape skins, has been shown to inhibit the formation of fatty deposits in the livers of rats. Resveratrol, along with the antifungal viniferins, may work together to protect the heart and the cardiovascular system.

French researchers report that red wine significantly lowered blood low-density lipoprotein (LDL), raising the beneficial high-density lipoprotein (HDL) cholesterol, possibly cleansing the arteries of fatty deposits. Among thirty wines tested, red Bordeaux was highest and white Bordeaux was among the lowest in resveratrol. Alcohol, like all phytochemicals and pharmaceuticals, can have a safe dose, a toxic dose, and a lethal dose. Ask Noah.

Red wine's ellagic acid may help prevent cancer. Resveratrol is reported to interfere with cancer, not at one phase, but at all three developmental phases. Part of this anticancer activity is attributed to cyclooxygenase inhibition by resveratrol. Cyclooxygenase inhibitors have been praised also for their antiarthritic activity. And it is the grape leaves that are much richer in this antiarthritic, anticancer, and anticardiac compound. These properties recommend the classical Middle Eastern stuffed grape leaves, heavily spiced with pepper and turmeric and containing rice, one of the resveratrol-rich cereals. A single glass of red wine, and you're eating not just good food, but good medicine.

FOLKLORE

The juice of unripe grapes acts as an astringent and eases throat afflictions.

Raisins are soothing, cooling, and sweet. They both stimulate the appetite and relieve constipation.

Recent headlines in the United States

proclaim that red wine shows some antiviral activity against herpes, more than white wine.

The sap of young vine branches has been used as a remedy for skin diseases.

Ayurvedics regard grapes, especially black grapes, as an aphrodisiac, diuretic, laxative, purgative, and refrigerant.

Grape vines are famous among survivalists for providing drinking water.

The Lebanese have a grape "cure" for fever, liver disorders, nervousness, smallpox, and tuberculosis. They feed small young grape leaves and tendrils to infants to prevent scurvy and iron deficiency. They grind the grape seeds and roots for an anemia treatment. The expressed grape leaf juice is applied to various skin conditions. Wine or its distillate is used by the Lebanese for cramps, stomachaches, toothaches, or, for that matter, for any pain.

In the Transvaal, grape syrup is used for diphtheria.

Grape seeds contain an edible oil also used in soaps and as a substitute for linseed (flax).

Henna

Lawsonia inermis L.

My beloved is to me a cluster of henna blossoms in the vineyards of En-gedi.

Song of Solomon 1:14

POSSIBLE BENEFITS

Cancer	*Rheumatism*
Dermatitis	*Sunburn*
Hives	

That sweet-talking Solomon compares his love to the beauty and fragrance of the henna flower (sometimes translated in Bible as camphire). Henna is one of the earliest known spices and perfumes. Henna dye has religious, utilitarian, mystical, and seductive powers. Henna is valued, especially by women of Egypt, for its powerful dark red dye that gives a brownish chestnut shade or turns hair black when mixed with indigo.

The leaves provide an important cosmetic dye. The young leaves are dried and ground into a powder, then soaked in water with a little lime juice to produce the dye. The leaves and twigs together produce a bright yellow, orange, or rusty red dye used on hair, palms of hands, soles of feet, finger and toe nails, and horse tails. Henna mixed with catechu produces a deep red color. The infusions also dye cotton, wool, and silk fabrics light reddish-brown. When exhumed, mummies entombed for three thousand years still retained traces of the dye used on their nails.

Henna flowers provide an astringent and stimulant for the skin. Henna is also effective against excessive perspiration.

Medicinally, the compound lawsone, contained in henna, is active against bacteria and fungi. A poultice of the leaves is applied to the scabs on fingers or toes where the nails have been lost due to fungal or viral infections.

Lawsonia inermis L.

*Fungicide for Finger
and Toe Nails*

To make a strong decoction, simmer five to
seven teaspoons of henna per cup of water for
20 minutes. Strain. After it cools, apply the
liquid to the affected area one to three times
a day with a cotton ball or clean cloth. Apply
daily until the fungal infection is gone.

FOLKLORE

Chewing the henna leaf is said to help
oral tumors.

Henna fruit oil and an ointment made
from the oil are folk remedies for the
hardening of the soft tissues of the liver
and diaphragm.

In India, the henna bark is believed
useful in combating and dissolving
kidney and urinary tract stones, skin

disorders, jaundice, leprosy, and
enlargement of the spleen or liver.

Cambodians drink a decoction of henna
root as a diuretic.

In Malaysia, a decoction of henna leaves
is used after childbirth and for beriberi,
rheumatism, skin disorders, stomach
disorders, and venereal disease.

Poultices made from henna leaves are
said to help various types of tumors and
show anticancer activity.

In Indonesia, henna leaves are used for
jaundice, leprosy, and scurvy.

Henna bark is given for jaundice and for

enlargement of spleen. It is an alternative treatment in skin diseases and leprosy.

Henna leaves also are used in the manufacture of perfumed oils and tanning agents.

Henna is used against herpes in Java.

Henna oil and essence are rubbed over the body to keep it cool.

In Arabic medicine, a henna bark decoction is used for jaundice and nervous symptoms.

Henna leaves are used as preventative medicine against skin disease.

Henna plants are grown as hedges throughout India. Wood from the henna plant is used to make tool handles, tent pegs, and other small articles.

Powdered henna seed is said to be a cerebral stimulant.

A decoction of henna leaves is used as an astringent gargle in sore throat.

Henna leaves act as a sedative.

Dried henna leaves are the source of a green powder used in cosmetics.

In India and Pakistan henna is widely

used by both men and women for coloring nails, fingers, hands, and hair. The women use it to stain the palms of their hands and soles of their feet.

Henna leaves are used for headaches, hemorrhages, milky vaginal discharge, excessive menstrual bleeding, abnormal and excessive loss of sperm, and typhoid.

An essential oil (mehndi oil) expressed from henna flowers has long been used in Indian perfumery.

The henna flowers are cooling; they reduce fevers and promote relaxation and sleep. The fruit is said to ease menstrual blood flow.

Horsemint

Mentha longifolia (L.) Huds.

Woe to you, scribes and Pharisees, hypocrites! For you tithe mint, dill, and cummin, and have neglected the weightier matters of the law: justice and mercy and faith. It is these you ought to have practiced without neglecting the others.

Matthew 23:23

POSSIBLE BENEFITS

Cold	*Impotence*
Dermatitis	*Pain*
Dyspepsia	*Rheumatism*
Headache	

Scriptures demanded that the Jews pay the tithe, or a tenth, of their crops or profits to the Temple. Jesus reminds the Pharisees that their obedience to the letter of the law does not relieve them of their duty to the spirit of the law.

Mint has been widely used for flavoring. The ancient Hebrews, Greeks, and Romans used mint. Writings dated from AD 37 state that mint was mentioned often in cooking recipes. The Jews served mint with their meat dishes, especially at the spring feast of the paschal lamb. Jews strewed synagogue floors with mint so that its perfume scented the place at each footfall.

There are many species of mints, and we cannot be certain which was popular or prolific in biblical times. Here are a few listed under English cultivar names: apple mint, spearmint, pennyroyal, pineapple mint, peppermint, and horsemint. One or more of these varieties of mint may contain compounds that could be as useful in treating Alzheimer's disease as do lemon balm, rosemary, and sage.

Mints and the essential oils of several

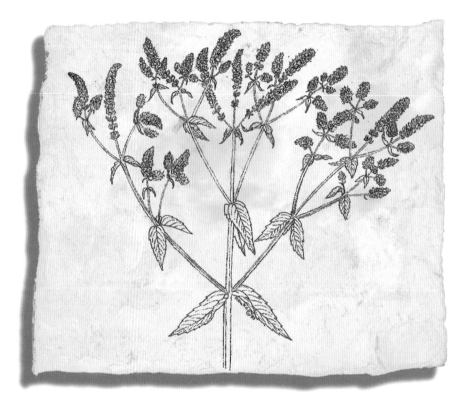

Mentha longifolia (L.) Huds.

species are used txo flavor candies, confectioneries, chewing gums and liqueurs. They also are ingredients in facial lotions, digestive aids, and toothpaste. Peppermint oil has shown anti-allergic activity. In aromatherapy peppermint stimulates brain activity and is a general pick-me-up. Aside from flavoring, the leaves have been used as a stimulant, emollient, ingredient for enemas, and a general pain remedy.

FOLKLORE

Pliny listed forty-one remedies attributed to mint.

Horsemint is used in folk remedies, often as an herbal tea, for apoplexy,

chest, colds, fever, headaches, stomachaches, and rheumatism.

At one time the English concluded that mint juice mixed with vinegar stirred up bodily lust.

Egyptian farmers made a tea from the flowering mint and leaves to treat flatulence.

Mint is added to hot baths to relieve skin ailments.

Hyssop

Origanum syriacum or *O. aegyptiacum*

Take a bunch of hyssop, dip it in the blood that is in the basin, and touch the lintel and the two doorposts with the blood in the basin. None of you shall go outside the door of your house until morning. For the LORD will pass through to strike down the Egyptians; when he sees the blood on the lintel and on the two doorposts, the LORD will pass over that door and will not allow the destroyer to enter your houses to strike you down.

Exodus 12:22–23

POSSIBLE BENEFITS

Colds	*Rheumatism*
Colic	*Sprains*
Polyps	*Swelling*

The hyssop of the Bible, also known as marjoram, is found growing in dry places among rocks. It has no relationship with the European hyssop. The leaves are used as a spice and medicinally as a tonic, antiflatulent, and digestive aid. An aromatic oil is obtained from the crushed and dried leaves.

Hyssop was tied into bunches and used to sprinkle the doorposts of the Israelites in Egypt with the blood of the paschal lamb so the angel of death would pass by that house. Hyssop was a plant of cleansing associated with purification ceremonies according to Mosaic law. The scriptures of Leviticus and Numbers especially express cleansing with hyssop after contact with the dead or lepers. The Hebrews also used hyssop to purify lepers and their houses. Hyssop has astringent qualities and the ability to cover odors. In the Middle Ages, when bathing was rare, hyssop was among the strewing herbs that was

152

stuffed in mattresses and scattered on floors and corridors. Its aromatic properties masked fetid odors.

FOLKLORE

In Lebanon hyssop tea is given to children suffering colds or colic. The Lebanese apply macerated leaves to rheumatic swellings and sprains.

In the British Herbal Pharmacopoeia, hyssop is recommended to treat bronchitis and the common cold.

Juniper

Juniperus oxycedrus L.

Send me also cedar, cypress, and algum timber from Lebanon, for I
know that your servants are skilled in cutting Lebanon timber.
My servants will work with your servants to prepare timber for me in
abundance, for the house I am about to build will be
great and wonderful.

2 Chronicles 2:8–9

POSSIBLE BENEFITS

Digestive stimulant	*Headaches*
Expectorant	*Poultice*

Algum timber is mentioned with that of cedars and cypresses. It likely belongs to a family of conifers that still grow in Israel today. Juniper has soft wood and grows to considerable size, producing excellent, fragrant timber. It has a shorter, shrubby relative called cade cedar. Juniper, or cade cedar, is valued as forest undergrowth, preventing erosion on steep mountainsides. Because of its spines, juniper protects tree seedlings from being devoured by grazing animals.

Two oils are processed from juniper berries or fruit: cade oil and refined cade oil. The refined oil is prized in men's fragrances; it gives a woody or smoky-leathery character to soaps and other toiletries. It also gives unsmoked fish and meats a smoked flavor. Cade oil is used in antiseptic soaps.

Medicinally, cade oil has a long history of treating parasitic skin diseases of animals. More recently, it has also been used for the human ailments eczema, psoriasis, and other dermatitis conditions. Cade oil is usually utilized in the form of an ointment, cream, or paste. Cade oil in shampoos may be prescribed for seborrhea, dermatitis of the scalp.

More recently, researchers have identified two compounds that have antiviral and anticancer potential. Many junipers contain deoxypodophyllotoxin-like lignans that could be used in the manufacture of the anticancer drug etoposide. Etoposide, used for treating testicular and lung cancers, currently is made from lignans found in the roots of the Asian mayapple. Deoxypodophyllotoxin is a potent antiviral compound that appears to inhibit several viruses, including those that cause flu and herpes.

FOLKLORE

Cade oil was administered internally and externally as a remedy for leprosy.

The Lebanese steep juniper berries in oil and take it for bladder and kidney ailments; in alcohol it is taken as an antiflatulent and a digestive aid; in water it is prescribed for jaundice and other liver ailments.

In Palestine, cade juniper yields a dark brown tar, or cade oil, used for healing skin ailments.

Cade oil was once used to treat corneal opacities, to allay pain in dental cavities, to kill head lice and their eggs, and for snakebite.

Cade oil has been recommended as a folk remedy for cancer, tumors, and malignant ulcers.

In the United States cade oil is classed as an irritant and not recommended for internal use.

Crushed juniper berries are applied as an antiseptic to wounds.

Cade oil is applied sparingly to old wounds and ulcers to promote healing.

In modern Europe, refined cade oil is taken internally as a dewormer—three to five drops in a little water, followed by a weak purgative.

North Africans consider juniper berries as a diuretic, stimulant, and as a dewormer.

Lentils

Lens culinaris Medik.

*Then Jacob gave Esau bread and lentil stew, and he ate and drank,
and rose and went his way. Thus Esau despised his birthright.*

Genesis 25:34

POSSIBLE BENEFITS

Fetal alcohol   *Spina bifida*
syndrome

Lentils are often referred to as Jacob's pottage. His twin brother Esau came in from the fields, starving, to where Jacob was cooking. In return for Esau's birthright, Jacob fed him some of "the red stuff" he was cooking.

In biblical times as today, dried lentils were cooked in stews and ground into flour and mixed with barley for bread. Lentils, along with barley and wheat, have been found in Syria, Iran, and Greece at sites dated earlier than 5000 BC. Along parts of the Nile, lentils are still the only breadstuff. In many countries lentils are a meat substitute. In India the young pods are served as a vegetable. The husks, dried leaves and stems, and bran are fed to livestock. Seeds are a source of commercial starch for the textile and printing industries. Medicinally, the healers recommend lentil seeds as a remedy for constipation and make hot poultices for ulcers.

Bread and lentil soup. That's good food and good medicine. Lentils are rich in genistein, an estrogenic compound thought to be effective against diabetic blindness and melanoma and other cancers. One of the better sources of folic acid, lentils also may be useful in preventing fetal alcohol syndrome and spina bifida. It has a better protein-fat ratio than soy (the lentil ratio is close to 20: 1 while that of soy is closer to 2:1). A pottage of lentils with caraway, cumin, garlic, and onion could be better medicine for the prevention of breast cancer than tamoxiphen or raloxiphen, and a great deal cheaper and healthier in other regards.

FOLKLORE

Lentils are supposed to remedy constipation and other intestinal afflictions.

Ethiopians use lentil seeds to counteract dysentery.

In Iraq, ground lentils are used to ease childbirth.

Ayurvedics use lentil seeds to treat excessive bile secretions, dysentery, eye ailments, heart ailments, skin diseases, painful and interrupted urination, and tumors.

In India, lentils are made into poultices for the ulcers that follow smallpox and for other slow-healing sores.

The Lebanese believe lentils are good for the anemia that follows dysentery. They cook a hot lentil soup, with or without onions, and apply it as a poultice to sores.

In Germany, lentil soup is used to facilitate the eruption in smallpox, then to poultice the skin ulcers resulting from smallpox.

Mandrake

Mandragora officinarum L.

Let us get up early to the vineyards; let us see if the vine flourish, whether the
tender grape appear, and the pomegranates bud forth: there will I give thee my love.
The mandrakes give a smell, and at our gates are all manner of pleasant fruits,
new and old, which I have laid up for thee, O my beloved.

Song of Solomon 7:12–13

POSSIBLE BENEFITS

Asthma	*Insomnia*
Cough	*Rheumatism*
Hay fever	*Vertigo*

CAUTION

Poisonous roots and fruit

Solomon's garden contains all sorts of delights: fruit- and scent-bearing trees, shrubs, herbs, and flowers. In this sensual setting, his garden would be incomplete without the infamous mandrakes, a symbol of fertility. The yellow, plum-like fruit has an unusual smell and sickeningly sweet taste.

The mandrake root resembles a human figure, which has led to its association with fertility rites as well as devil worship. The mandrake root is esteemed for its narcotic properties. Related to the potato, it is a member of the nightshade family. The mandrake plant is slightly poisonous. The fruit, eaten in quantity, produces dizziness and may cause insanity. Mandrakes contain the major alkaloids, atropine and scopolamine (you may already be familiar with scopolamine if you have a tendency to get carsick, seasick, or airsick). Taken in high enough quantities, atropine suppresses the central nervous system, while the scopolamine acts as a powerful hypnotic and slows the heart rate. It can eventually result in death.

Mandragora officinarum L.

What draws us to the mandrake is not its medical properties but our fascination with its history of superstition. Jews considered the mandrake a charm against evil spirits. Josephus related a Jewish legend that the Jews tied a dog to the mandrake plant to pull it out of the ground because to touch a fresh mandrake would kill a man. The mandrake

What draws us to the mandrake is not its medical properties but our fascination with its history of superstition.

shrieked, the dog died, and the root was rendered harmless thereafter. Arabs call the mandrake "devil's apples" because of its supposed powers to excite voluptuousness. We call it "apples of love" for precisely the same reason.

It has a long fame for use in love potions and incantations. As late as 1630 in Hamburg, Germany, three women were executed for possession of mandrake root, supposed "evidence" that they were involved in witchcraft. The witches of Salem, Massachusetts, likely anointed themselves with the pulp of the mandrake fruit, perhaps even greasing their broomsticks, and the alkaloid reaction induced the sensation of flying and other hallucinations. In one hallucination, lycanthropy, the subject imagines turning into a wolf.

The mandrake has a large root, dark brown and rugged, resembling the human body. Once esteemed for its medicinal and narcotic properties, the mandrake's properties have been eclipsed by its use as an aphrodisiac and its orgiastic and magical applications among cults involving the sexes. In the proper, trained hands it can still serve as an anesthetic, an enema, a fever reducer, sedative, and stimulant.

FOLKLORE

Scopolamine-containing plants have been used as anesthetics for centuries in traditional Chinese medicine.

Fresh mandrake roots were once used for inducing sleep when someone was in continuous pain, convulsions, or rheumatic pain.

Crushed mandrake leaves and boiled roots were used to treat tumors.

Boiled in milk, mandrake roots were poulticed onto benign ulcers.

Mixed with brandy, mandrake roots are used for chronic rheumatism.

Milk Thistle

Silybum marianum (L.) Gaertn.

*[T]horns and thistles it shall bring forth for you;
and you shall eat the plants of the field.*

Genesis 3:18

POSSIBLE BENEFITS

Alcoholism	Hepatitis
Asthma	Jaundice
Cirrhosis	Psoriasis
Kidney, urinary	
tract stones	

We aren't certain that milk thistle is one of the thorns, thistles, and briers referred to in the Bible, but it could be. We know that the milk thistle grows among shrubs that are common in Samaria and parts of Israel today. A charming legend from medieval Europe holds that the white mottling on the leaves of the milk thistle plant was caused by a drop of the Virgin Mary's milk, giving the plant the name Our Lady's thistle or *marianum*. In Rome, Pliny wrote that consuming milk thistle carried off bile. The English herbalist Culpepper suggested that it was good for jaundice and for removing liver obstructions.

Milk thistle has been used as a liver remedy for 2,000 years. Liver disease (often a deadly side effect of alcoholism) attacks the blood's filtration system, allowing dangerous toxins to accumulate in the body. Milk thistle containing silymarin seems to be the most promising natural compound both for preventing damage to the liver and for correcting a damaged liver. Studies show that it has even been able to regenerate damaged liver cells. Research studies led Commission

Silybum marianum (L.) Gaertn.

E, the German expert panel that judges the safety and effectiveness of medicinal herbs for the German government, to approve milk thistle seeds and seed extracts as supportive treatment for cirrhosis and chronic inflammatory liver conditions. Silymarin also helps protect the liver from many industrial toxins, like carbon tetrachloride. Even if you don't have liver damage or disease, milk

A charming legend from medieval Europe holds that the white mottling on the leaves of the milk thistle plant was caused by a drop of the Virgin Mary's milk . . .

thistle helps improve liver functions by aiding the removal of toxins from the body.

Recently, silymarin has shown great promise as a diabetes fighter. In 1998 an Italian scientist suggested that taking 600 mg of silymarin daily substantially reduced diabetic symptoms and complications. An article in the *Journal of Hepatology* said that taking silymarin lowered blood sugar and insulin levels.

If you are a gardener, you can grow milk thistles. Very young leaves of the herb can be used in salads; however, the leaves contain only traces of silymarin. Silymarin is effective in helping to prevent or alleviate gallstones. Milk thistle seeds also contain eight anti-inflammatory compounds helpful in relieving skin infections and disorders such as psoriasis.

I enjoy munching the seeds like sunflower seeds and entertain a fantasy in which I produce and market the milk thistle seeds as "beer nuts" to serve in bars where the drinkers are worried about their livers but don't have enough sense to taper off their alcohol intake.

FOLKLORE

Milk thistle heads were once eaten like artichokes.

The seed oil extracted from milk thistle has promising food or industrial lubrication applications.

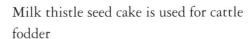

Milk thistle seed cake is used for cattle fodder

Milk thistle seeds have served as coffee substitutes.

Muskmelon

Cucumis melo L.

["]We remember the fish we used to eat in Egypt for nothing, the cucumbers, the melons, the leeks, the onions, and the garlic; but now our strength is dried up, and there is nothing at all but this manna to look at."

Numbers 11:5–6

POSSIBLE BENEFITS

Cancer

Dyspepsia

Excessive menstrual bleeding

Eczema

Freckles

Some think the biblical melon was muskmelon, others the watermelon. Both are cultivated as pleasantly juicy fruits in a dry country. Fruits are eaten fresh out of the rind after removing of seeds or as dessert sprinkled with sugar or powdered ginger. Fruits of some melons are used for preserves or as vegetables. Melon seeds are edible and yield an edible oil.

The entire melon plant enjoys a medical reputation. Melon fruit is used in a lotion to treat eczema and to remove tan and freckles. The rind is said to help reduce tumors of the stomach and treat uterine cancer. The root, boiled with pinewood, is said to be a cure for stomach, bladder, and uterine cancers. Dietary use of the pulp or the seeds is believed by some to help tumors (especially of the bladder, liver, and stomach). Melon seeds have been recommended for stomach cancer and inflammatory ailments of the digestive tract. An extract of melon oil is suggested to relieve painful menstruation. Melon flowers cause vomiting, but the stalks help relieve vomiting. Powdered buds are used for jaundice and nasal ulcers. Medical research has barely taken a slice of the curative potential of melons.

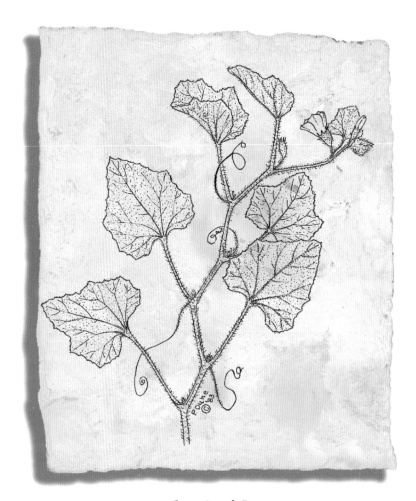

Cucumis melo L.

FOLKLORE

The Chinese use the melon peduncles (the flower stems or stalks) for skin eruptions and dyspepsia.

In North Africa melon fruiting peduncles are regarded as emetic and expectorant.

Some think that melon rind rubbed into the skin can help prevent sunstroke.

In Ayurvedic medicine, melon fruit is regarded as aphrodisiac, diuretic, laxative, and tonic. It is used for biliousness, fatigue, and insanity.

The melon fruit is a digestive stimulant; the seeds relieve digestive upset.

Lebanese mothers rub the pulp on their breast when they are weaning their babies.

Lebanese believe melon seeds repel bedbugs.

Myrrh

Cistus inanus creticus, Commiphora erythraea (Ehrenb.) Engl.

The turn came for each girl to go in to King Ahasuerus, after being twelve months under the regulations for the women, since this was the regular period of their cosmetic treatment, six months with oil of myrrh and six months with perfumes and cosmetics for women.

Esther 2:12

POSSIBLE BENEFITS

Analgesic

Astringent

Bronchitis

Expectorant

High cholesterol

 King Ahasuerus found his captive Esther a comely lass and selected her as a future wife. Only a king or the very rich could afford to use myrrh so lavishly. Such perfumes and cosmetics could hardly have been a part of Esther's life as a slave.

There are 135 species of myrrh found throughout Africa and Arabia, growing mainly in very arid regions. In her book *All the Plants of the Bible*, Winifred Walker asserts that the myrrh mentioned in the Old Testament came from a small plant that grew among the sand and rocks, called a rockrose. The gum collected from the rockrose was pressed into cakes and used as perfume. In the New Testament the soft dark resin collected and sold in golden spiral pieces, sometimes called "tears" or "pearls," was from a small tree. Myrrh was sold as a spice or an ingredient of the anointing oil used in the Tabernacle or as a salve for the purification of the dead. The stems and leaves were used to prepare perfume and incense, a practice that continues in Eastern churches today. Medicinally, the extract served as a salve, stimulant, or expectorant.

So many legends abound about the origins and use of myrrh. Myrrh was one of the

Commiphora erythraea (Ehrenb.) Engl.

three gifts of the Magi to the baby Jesus: gold, frankincense, and myrrh, the latter foretelling how Jesus would suffer and die. The term *myrrophore* was applied to the women who bore spices to the sepulcher of Jesus—aloes, cassia, and cinnamon. In Mesopotamia and the Greco-Roman worlds, myrrh was a panacea for almost every human affliction from earaches to hemorrhoids. The Asians esteemed myrrh as an astringent tonic taken internally and as a cleansing agent applied externally. At Heliopolis myrrh was burned at noon as incense for the Egyptian sun god. Persian kings wore myrrh in their crowns. An old legend says that Myrrha, daughter of the King of Cyprus, became unnaturally obsessed with her Father. He exiled her to the Arabian desert, where the gods transformed her into the myrrh tree "in which guise she remains, weeping tears perfumed of repentance."

Where real medicine begins and folk medicine ends in the literature is not readily apparent. Among herbalists a salve of myrrh used as a analgesic can assuage the discomfort of topical ulcerations. Much of the commerce in myrrh today comes from closely related species of myrrh from Arabia, Ethiopia, and Somalia. Myrrh makes into a good mouthwash for spongy gums, ulcerated throats, and mouth sores. It has been found helpful in treating bronchial inflammations and vaginal infections. Gugul, or Indian myrrh, has been the subject of recent research in leukemia and blood cholesterol levels. So far, tests on laboratory rats show that phytochemicals in gugul

In Mesopotamia and the Greco-Roman worlds, myrrh was a panacea for almost every human affliction from earaches to hemorrhoids.

attack and destroy the build-up of white blood cells as well as reducing the levels of serum cholesterol in the blood.

Today myrrh oil is an astringent in mouthwash and gargles as well as a fixative or fragrance in creams, detergents, lotions, perfumes, and soaps. Myrrh has been approved by the FDA for food use in alcoholic beverages, baked goods, gelatins, and puddings. Myrrh gum makes a good mucilage, and the insoluble residue from the tincture can be used as a glue.

Whatever plant the biblical myrrh actually was, it was presented as a gift because of its great value to the people of that time. With all its uses, it may be just as valuable in our time.

FOLKLORE

Tanzanians make a tea from the bark of myrrh to treat diarrhea and stomachaches and to speed up parturition.

The Chinese apply myrrh to relieve spasms and stimulate digestive fluids.

Kenyans chew the myrrh gum.

In the Ivory Coast a decoction brewed

from the bark of myrrh cures male infertility.

Africans chew myrrh stems to cleanse the teeth.

Ghanaians fumigate their clothing with the fragrant smoke of the burning myrrh wood.

Algerians dress oozing open wounds with myrrh resin.

Egyptian women carry the "pearls" of myrrh in their handbags as a perfume.

Myrrh shrubs survive cutting so well it is a symbol of immortality among the Tuareg.

Ethiopians eat the myrrh roots raw.

Ugandans pound the unripe seeds and add water to make a warming beverage.

West Africans use myrrh as an insecticide to repel termites.

Nigerians plant the spiny myrrh shrub as a fence hedge.

Myrrh bark is a good source of tannin.

Myrrh wood has various uses from firewood to tool handles and wood utensils.

Myrrh wood and seeds are used in necklaces.

Extract from the bark of myrrh trees is an insecticide.

In Nigeria a myrrh decoction is used to treat insanity and tapeworm.

Myrtle

Myrtus communis L.

Then they spoke to the angel of the LORD who was standing among the myrtle trees,
"We have patrolled the earth, and lo, the whole earth remains at peace."

Zechariah 1:11

POSSIBLE BENEFITS

Asthma	*Polyps*
Bronchitis	*Smallpox*
Cancer	*Tuberculosis*
Hemorrhoids	

Myrtle is a symbol of peace, divine blessing or divine generosity, and justice. Jews collect myrtle branches to decorate sheds or booths during the Feast of the Tabernacles, or Sukkot. Sprigs with three leaves in a whorl (which are not common) are especially sought after.

Myrtle comes from Greek meaning "perfume" and in Hebrew *hadas* means "sweetness." Many plant names are also names of people or places. Mordecai adopts Esther and calls her Hadassah, the Hebrew imagey for peace and joy.

Greeks considered myrtle a symbol of love and immortality. They crowned their priests, heroes, and outstanding men with myrtle. In Babylonia the myrtle tree also designated the women who were brides. In the bazaars of Jerusalem and Damascus, the flowers, leaves, and fruits were sold for making perfume. Arabs say that myrtle is one of the three plants taken from the Garden of Eden because of its fragrance. When crushed, the leaves and young branches give off a pleasant aroma. It was used in perfumes and helped mask less pleasant odors.

The wood has been used for walking sticks, furniture, and tool handles. The leaf provided spice, perfume, and bridal wreaths

Myrtus communis L.

for virgins. The berry was used as an aromatic food flavoring, a wine-like drink, and as a breath sweetener. The oil from the leaf was an antiflatulent.

Myrtle has been grown since ancient times for the fragrant, aromatic flowers, leaves, and bark. The leaves are used in massage to work up a glowing skin. A fragrant oil obtained from these is used in perfumery. Oil of myrtle can be used to great culinary advantage as a replacement for dried myrtle leaves in several meat dishes, particularly for table sauces. The essential oil also is used in toilet waters or colognes. The purplish-black berries or fruits, known as *mursins*, have medicinal value and are edible. In Italy myrtle leaves are used as a spice; in Syria all parts of the plant are dried for perfume. Around Rabat they mix the leaves with shampoo to darken the hair. In some parts of Europe the leaves are used to make a tea. Green and dried fruits sometimes are used as condiments. The wood is very hard; its texture and grain are unique. The plants make a nice evergreen hedge, appropriate for the Mediterranean climate. It grows on hillsides in Israel, especially near Bethlehem and Hebron and in the Plain of Jezreel near Mounts Carmel and Tabor.

Myrtle contains antibacterial phenols. Medicinally, an infusion or tincture of leaves treats such disorders as a dropped uterus or milky vaginal discharge. The tincture of myrtle is an antibacterial wash to cleanse incisions and relieve swollen joints. And it is used to check night sweats and for all types of pulmonary disorders.

FOLKLORE

Turkish and Russian leather is tanned with myrtle bark and roots, which impart a distinctive odor to the leather.

Myrtle was sacred to Venus as a symbol of sensual love and passion.

Myrtle is placed on Bohemian caskets as a symbol of immortality.

The Lebanese consider myrtle both binding and diuretic, believing it holds loose things in place (e.g., the bowels, the emotions, or the teeth).

Myrtle berries and seeds are said to cure tumors and uterine fibroids.

The essential oil from myrtle is added to plasters or unguents that help reduce or relieve tumors of the breast and genitals.

Iranians make a hot poultice from myrtle leaves to apply to boils.

Algerians recommend an infusion of myrtle leaves to relieve asthma.

North Africans use the dry myrtle flower buds to treat smallpox

Nettle

Urtica dioica L.

Among the bushes they bray; under the nettles they huddle together.
A senseless, disreputable brood, they have been whipped out of the land.

Job 30:7–8

POSSIBLE BENEFITS

Allergy	*Prostatitis*
Arthritis	*Rheumatism*
Hay fever	

The nettle shrubs in the Book of Job must have grown quite tall for the dispossessed to have hid beneath them. The Latin name for nettles' genus, *Urtica*, means "to burn." The microscopic hairs on nettle leaves are responsible for the itchy, burning feeling it causes and for its most common name, "stinging" nettles.

Chemically, the poison is very similar to that of bee stings and snake venom. Because of its sting, nettles were used widely in metaphors, especially to describe uninhabitable lands and forbidding landscapes.

One of the earliest fibers in Europe came from the nettle stems that were used to produce muslin cloth. During wartime when other fibers were not available, nettle fiber was used to make both textiles and paper. Similar to hemp or flax, nettle fiber can be spun into fine or coarse materials.

Many people in several different regions of the world believe that microinjections of nettle alleviate arthritis. Science has not yet proven this, but when different people independently arrive at the same conclusion, there just might be some truth in their findings.

Nettles are rich in vitamins A, C, and E and in the antioxidants that can help prevent cancers. As a matter of fact, nettle is quite nutritious. Young nettle tops can be used as a spring green vegetable prepared like spinach.

Urtica dioica L.

In your recipe for spinach lasagna, substitute young nettle leaves for the spinach. In Scotland, nettles are combined with leeks or onions, broccoli or cabbage, and rice in a muslin bag; the bag is boiled and the vegetable dish is served with butter or gravy.

FOLKLORE

In Algeria, nettles are powdered and mixed with powdered jasmine to treat gonorrhea.

Nettle leaves inspired the design of Corinthian capitals in Greek architecture.

In Sweden and Russia, nettles are sometimes cultivated as a fodder plant.

Dried nettles can be fed to livestock and poultry, but few animals will eat the living plants.

In Russia, nettle leaves are steeped in alcohol to make a preparation for chronic hepatitis, gallbladder, and habitual constipation.

Alcoholic extracts of nettle, chamomile, thyme, and burdock have been used in hair and scalp preparations.

In Russia, nettles give a green pigment to candies, pastries, and other confections.

Olive

Olea europaea L.

*[A]nd if the root is holy, then the branches also are holy. But if
some of the branches were broken off, and you, a wild olive shoot, were grafted in
their place to share the rich root of the olive tree, do not boast over the branches.
If you do boast, remember that it is not you that support the root,
but the root that supports you.*

Romans 11:16–18

POSSIBLE BENEFITS

Cancer	*Hypertension*
Dermatitis	*Sore throats*
Heart disease	*Sunburn*

Slow-growing olive trees can live as long as 1,000 years or more, but they cannot be neglected. For an olive tree to produce good fruit it must be grafted. A twig from a highly productive specimen is grafted onto a sturdy, rapidly growing trunk to maintain an efficient orchard. Improper grafting produces poor fruit. This practice of grafting is the metaphor found in Paul's letters to the Romans. Through faith, gentiles and Jews are branches of the olive tree (representing Israel) that is rooted in God's power and love.

The olive tree has been cultivated for more than 6,000 years. The tree and its most import product, olive oil, were as valuable as gold in the Levant. Olive oil is symbolic of goodness and purity, and the tree is a symbol of peace and happiness. Many references to gardens in Scripture seem to refer to olive groves. Jesus spent his last night of freedom in the Garden of Gethsemane, which means "the garden with the olive press." In ancient

Galen's
Cereatum Refrigerans

Melt beeswax in olive oil (56% olive oil,
24.5% beeswax, 14.5% water, and 5%
herb water, perhaps rose water)

Add herb extracts (see the list below)

Make an emulsion and apply to the face
and skin to both cool and soften. A pinch of
borax makes emulsion whiter and helps set
it. You can substitute almond oil for olive
oil; almond oil makes the skin even softer
and smoother.

Good skin-care herbs include: yarrow,
rosemary, mint, orange peel, lavender, gera-
nium, hyssop, calendula, chamomile, and
elder flowers.

Israel the oil was extracted by pressing the
fruit with a vertical round millstone or olive
press.

The oil has sacred uses for anointing and
sacrifices. Passages where the word *anoint* appears usually mean "anoint with olive oil."
Anointing with olive oil is also soothing and
comforting in dry, arid climates. The Hebrew
word for anoint is *mesiach*, or "messiah." The
Greek word ΧΡΙΣΤΨΣ or *christos* was the practice of "dubbing oil" on athletes following

competition. Hence, we get the words *Christ*
or *Messiah*, which confirms why only olive oil
could be used for anointing in the Temple.

Daan Smit relates in his book *Plants of the
Bible: A Gardener's Guide* that the "gardens" in
the Middle East consisted of fruit- and nut-
bearing trees rather than flowers. The gardens,
groves of olive and fig trees, were surrounded
by thorny hedges or stone walls. The gardens
of royalty and the wealthy also would have almond, walnut, pistachio, other trees, and various herbs. Just as with vineyards, there was
usually a tower in every orchard, from which
a guard would keep out wild animals or
thieves.

The hard wood, which is richly grained,
has been used in construction as well as in
cabinet making and for ornaments and
kitchen utensils. The leaves were woven into
wreaths. The bark was used medicinally to
heal wounds and the leaves decocted into an
astringent and lotion to reduce fevers.

Olive oil was the base of perfumed ointments sold in classical Athens and Rome.
Galen (AD 130–200), considered along with
Hippocrates as one of the best physicians of
ancient times, wrote the first systematic scientific cosmetic book, "Galen's of Rome." He
produced a *cereatum refrigerans*, a cream or

cooling ointment, that was the rage of ancient Rome.

Approximately 90 percent of the world production of olives is for the oil extracted by crushing its fruit. The remaining 10 percent provides table olives: black olives, treated in a brine solution for three to nine months, and green olives, fermented in lactic acid. Olive pumice, the residue left after milling the stones, or seeds, for oil, is used in animal feeds. The stones are used in the manufacture of molded products and plastics.

Olive oil is recommended for patients recovering from heart attacks when other oils are rigidly excluded from their diets. Olive contains the antitumor compound sitosterol-d-glucoside. Olive oil does for the heart and arteries what it does for the skin: it keeps them healthy and supple.

Dandruff Relief

Olive oil shows up in many conditioners, moisturizers, and shampoos. It is also an excellent medium for herbal extraction: add four heaping handfuls (almost 80 grams) of finely chopped herbs to a cup of olive oil; let the infusion steep in sunshine for two weeks. Filter the mixture through cheesecloth, bottle, and store in the refrigerator. Olive oil mixed with witch hazel revitalizes dry, dull hair; it makes a good hair tonic that also relieves burns and stings. Warm the olive oil and rub it into your hair for a healthy scalp. Try the following recipe to relieve dandruff or chronic itchy scalp.

Heat balm of Gilead buds and rosemary in olive oil.

When the mixture is cool, rub into the scalp before going to sleep. (Use double pillow cases.)

Wash hair in the morning.

FOLKLORE

In Italy, an olive branch is hung over the door to keep out evil spirits.

The Lebanese use olive oil for burns, colds, constipation, lesions, stomachaches, sore throats, and sunburn.

Algerians chew olive leaves to relieve toothaches and oral sores caused by excess tobacco usage.

Iranians use a decoction of olive leaves for coughs.

Olive oil is applied as an emollient to relieve dermatitis and swellings.

Olive leaves, pounded in wine and made into a poultice, are said to cure tumors.

Onion

Allium cepa L.

We remember the fish we used to eat in Egypt for nothing, the cucumbers, the melons, the leeks, the onions, and the garlic; but now our strength is dried up, and there is nothing at all but this manna to look at.

Numbers 11:5–6

POSSIBLE BENEFITS

Angina	*Diabetes*
Cancer	*Hypertension*

Although widely used in ancient and modern Israel, the onion is mentioned only once in the Bible. There are more than 500 species of onions, some edible and some ornamental. Onions are represented in many Egyptian tomb paintings. They were found in the breasts of mummies, and onion peels were found on the ears and eyes. Onions were considered a necessity in the diets of the workers building the pyramids.

Onions have for millennia been famous for food, as a condiment, and as medicine. Green onions are eaten raw or cooked with meats, fish, or cheese. They are a vegetable chopped up and added to cottage cheese and salads. Dried onions are added when fresh onions are not available. Onions are good boiled, baked, creamed, broiled, fried, french-fried, pickled, or raw. For my taste, onions are mandatory in soups, stews, dressings, and salads.

Onion shares most of its real and folk medicinal attributes with garlic and other members of the *Allium* species. Onions contain many of the same sulfur compounds that make garlic such a treasure house. But onion has a few different chemicals (each plant

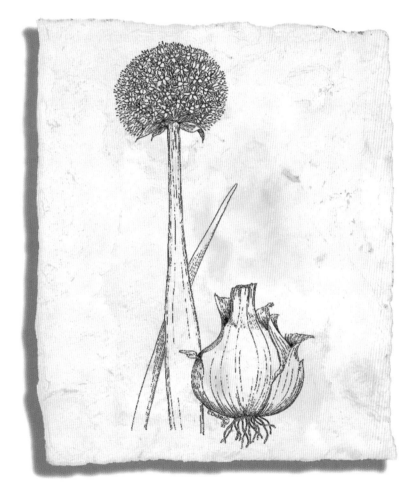

Allium cepa L.

species is chemically distinct from others). It is much richer in quercetin than garlic. Quercetin inhibits the growth of cancer cells

> *Onion shares most of its real and folk medicinal attributes with garlic and other members of the* Allium *species.*

in breast, colon, intestinal, and ovarian tumors as well as leukemia. I add both onions and garlic to all my soups and most of my salads, hoping to stave off cancer, heart disease, and diabetes. Allicin, a compound found in both garlic and onion, is antiseptic, hyperglycemic, hypocholesterolemic, insecticidal, and larvicidal. Another compound of many attributes, rutin, is reported to prevent cancer as well as protect against radiation.

We dissect food in laboratories to isolate major bioactive compounds. Then we try to recreate these compounds and label them as "active ingredients" in manufactured medicines. But it is really the synergy, "the symphony of nutrients working synergistically," that provides the great healing power of whole foods. I'd rather take bean soup with onions and garlic to help prevent coronary heart disease and cancer of the breast and bowels than manufactured pills.

FOLKLORE

Freshly expressed onion juice is said to be moderately bactericidal.

Onion bulbs are said to be an aphrodisiac.

Onion skins produce a dye for yarn and Easter eggs.

Onions are alleged to speed healing of gunshot wounds and cure scorpion bites.

Onion scales contain a heart stimulant that increases the pulse volume and reduces blood sugar.

Onion juice is used for coughs and earaches.

Roasted onions are applied to tumors.

In Iran and Iraq onions are boiled with

sugar and almond oil as a purgative during typhoid fever epidemics.

Onion seed mixed with honey is a folk remedy for warts.

An injection of onion juice is said to help cancers of the breast and rectum.

The onion bulb is said to relieve swollen glands and tumors.

Pomegranate

Punica granatum L.

Saul was staying in the outskirts of Gibeah under the pomegranate tree
that is at Migron; the troops that were with him were about six hundred men . . .

1 Samuel 14:2

POSSIBLE BENEFITS

Bronchitis	*Infertility*
Cancer	*Mouth sores*
Dysentery	*Painful menstruation*
Estrogen deficiency	*Sore throat*
Hemorrhoids	*Worms*
Inflammation of the inner eyelid	

The pomegranate was the main metaphor for fertility throughout the ancient Near East. According to Jewish legend, there are approximately 613 seeds in the pomegranate: the same as the number of laws God gave to Israel. The number of Saul's troops and the number of God's laws make a powerful metaphor. *Pomegranate* literally means "apple with grains," referring to the many clear ruby-colored seeds found in each fruit, covered with a thin skin and full of juice. Is this another candidate for the tree of knowledge from the Garden of Eden?

Pomegranate has been cultivated in Egypt and Palestine since time immemorial. In the Book of Joshua, pomegranate was a proper name for places. In Numbers it was among the fruit brought back by spies sent out by Moses. The flowers, bark, and rind produced a red dye particularly effective on leather. The Moors introduced both the pomegranate and the method of tanning leather with the juice to Spain. The result is Cordovan leather, that deep, rich, blood-red color. The calyx of the fruit later served as a pattern for the crowns of the Torah, called *rimonim*. The First Book of Kings and Jeremiah de-

Punica granatum L.

scribe that the fruit was used as a motif for the capitals of Solomon's temple. In Exodus the hems of the high priests' robes were embroidered with pomegranate designs. The juice was often mingled with wine. The seeds were prescribed medicinally against tapeworm, while the rind served as an astringent for skin problems and diarrhea.

Pomegranates are high in potassium and dietary fiber. They also contain vitamin C, most B vitamins, copper, pantothenic acid, magnesium, and phosphorus, with less than 1 gram fat and only 105 calories per pomegranate. The fruit, said to cure various types of tumors, contains tannins as well as betulinic, gallic, and ursolic acids, all recognized as experimental antitumor agents.

A syrup known as grenadine is made from the seeds. The first sherbet was a preparation of pomegranate juice mixed with snow. Apothecaries used the blossoms, known as balausts, in the preparation of an astringent medicine for treating dysentery. The acid pulp surrounds the seeds, the edible portion of the fruit. They are used in salads or as table fruit, or made into beverages or jellies. Pomegranate fruits ferment easily, and wine is made from the seeds. It was usually added to grape wine in biblical times. Egyptians today still make pomegranate wine and other beverages.

Pomegranate is the best-known plant source of estrone, an estrogen hormone.

The seeds were prescribed medicinally against tapeworm, while the rind served as an astringent for skin problems and diarrhea.

Current research suggest that estrogen replacement slashes the risk of coronary heart disease and may decrease the risk of colon cancer, tooth loss, bone loss, and Alzheimer's disease. Add the seeds of one fruit to a blender full of iced lemonade for an antiosteoporosis beverage. It's cheaper than what Upjohn has to offer and a very cool way to relieve hot flashes. As a side note, other plants known to contain significantly high doses of boron that can aid men and women prone to osteoporosis are leafy green vegetables, plums, and prunes. Doesn't a glass of pomegranate juice or cup of grenadine sherbet sound lovely right now?

FOLKLORE

In Syria and Iran pomegranate fruit is cut open, seeded, strewn with sugar, and sprinkled with rose water.

Pomegranate rinds are used for tanning Morocco leather, giving it a yellow color. Pomegranate flowers give a red dye.

Pomegranate is the national flower emblem of Spain.

Women in various parts of the world stain their teeth red eating pomegranate flowers. Polynesians dye their teeth black with the rind.

In China, pomegranates symbolize fertility; women offer pomegranates to the goddess of mercy in the hope of being blessed with children.

Ayurvedics use the pomegranate rind for diarrhea, dysentery, and worms, the bark and seeds for bronchitis. They use the ripe fruit as an astringent and aphrodisiac.

Filipinos gargle with a decoction of pomegranate leaves for oral ailments.

Pomegranates made good ornamental hedges, especially in dry climates. The plants are also useful as a greenhouse potted plant. Cut flowers are long-lasting in arrangements.

Iranians use pomegranate flowers in a concoction to relieve painful gums.

Pomegranate leaf juices inhibit some viruses.

Poppy

Papaver somniferum L.

And when they came to a place called Golgotha (which means Place of a Skull), they offered him wine to drink, mixed with gall; but when he tasted it, he would not drink it.

Matthew 27:33–34

POSSIBLE BENEFITS

Cancer	*Insomnia*
Cough	*Pain*
Dysentery	*Toothache*
Impotence	

The poppy plant provides a narcotic, sometimes called gall, that induces sleep, a sleep so heavy that the person becomes insensible. One of the onlookers at Golgotha (whether one of the mob, a Roman soldier, or one of Jesus' followers) took pity on the prisoner on the cross. He added gall or poppy juice to the potion of sour wine or vinegar offered to the dying man.

The opium poppy is not named in the Bible, but it was used extensively in the ancient world for a variety of reasons. Opium was used in cult rituals, to seal wine jugs, or for recreational imbibing. Jewish authorities maintain that the plant and its stupefying effects were well known among the ancient Israelites more than 2,000 years ago. In the Talmud *The Jerushalmi* warned against opium eating. Egyptians claim to become more cheerful, talkative, and industrious following the eating of opium. When falling asleep, they would have visions of "orchards and pleasure gardens embellished with many trees, herbs, and various flowers."

The blooming season for opium poppies lasts only a few short weeks, but what a riot of color they offer the landscape, dancing and fluttering in the breezes. While nearly all parts of the poppy plant contain a white milky juice or latex, the unripe capsules, containing the juice in abundance, are used for extraction of opium. Opium is mainly used

---

The blooming season for opium poppies lasts only a few short weeks, but what a riot of color they offer the landscape, dancing and fluttering in the breezes.

---

for the manufacture of morphine, codeine, laudanum, and other alkaloids. Opium is the air-dried, milky extract obtained from excised unripe fruits. Its compounds are used in medicine as analgesic, anodyne, antispasmodic, hypnotic, narcotic, sedative, as respiratory depressant, and to relieve severe pain.

Poppies are native to the Mediterranean region and eastward to Iran. Poppies are now cultivated in many tropical, subtropical, and warm temperate countries. Poppies thrive in rich, well-manured soil, in hot-to-warm regions. The peony-flowered opium poppy is widely grown as an ornamental, even in the United States, where it is illegal to grow.

Poppy seeds contain no opium and are used extensively in baking and sprinkling on rolls and bread. They are also a good source of energy. Seeds are the source of a drying oil, used in the manufacture of paints, varnishes, and soaps. Although the seeds contain no narcotic alkaloids, urinalysis following their ingestion may incorrectly indicate morphine or heroin misuse.

The plant, boiled in oil, is said to aid hardened soft tissue and tumors of the liver. A tincture of the plant is said to help cancerous ulcers. Smoking the plant is said to cure cancer of the tongue. The capsule decoction is said to cure uterine cancer. An injection of the seed decoction is also said to help uterine cancer.

FOLKLORE

Algerians tamp opium into tooth cavities to relieve toothaches.

Lebanese used opium poppies to quiet excitable people and to relieve toothaches, headaches, and incurable pain.

Iranians use the seeds for nosebleeds.

Iranians eat the seedlings as a potherb.

In Ayurvedic medicine, poppy seeds are considered aphrodisiac, constipating, and tonic.

Rue

Ruta graveolens L.

But woe to you Pharisees! For you tithe mint and rue and herbs of all kinds,
and neglect justice and the love of God; it is these you ought to have practiced,
without neglecting the others.

Luke 11:42

POSSIBLE BENEFITS

Colic	*Hysteria*
Cramps	*Piebald skin*
Dyspepsia	*Rheumatism*
Epilepsy	

CAUTION

Poisonous

Jesus accepts an invitation to dinner with a certain Pharisee. When Jesus does not wash (a before-dinner ritual), the Pharisee rebukes him. Jesus reminds the Pharisees that if Jesus washes the outside of cup and leaves the inside unwashed, Jesus still has a dirty cup. So it is with the Pharisee; he follows the ritual of washing, but his soul is still unclean because the Pharisee pursues questionable business practices.

Rue, mentioned only once in the Bible, is a valuable herb. Pliny mentions honeyed wine flavored with rue, as well as eighty-four remedies containing rue. Fresh or dried leaves are used sparingly to season such foods as cheese, vegetable juice, salads, stews, and vegetables. (When dried, rue loses its aroma but not its taste.) Rue's Latin name *graveolens* means "strong smelling." In ancient times court officials took advantage of the disinfectant and aromatic properties of rue. They scattered rue around the courts of justice to protect officials from the stench and fevers that prisoners

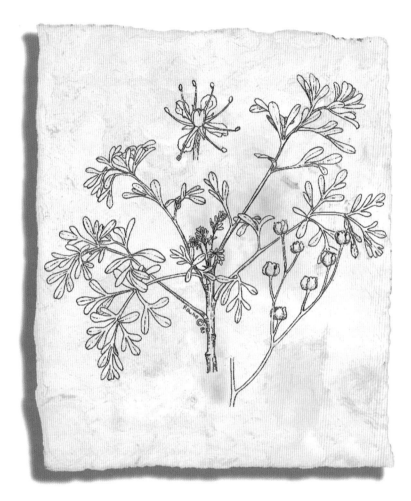

Ruta graveolens L.

brought to the court from their jail cells. The highly aromatic leaves were used as a condiment. Medicinally, it was prescribed against insects and snakebites.

Rue was highly prized as a medicinal herb in ancient times. Centuries ago it was considered to be a preventative against many contagious diseases. It was even believed that rue could drive out an incipient disease if the patient simply inhaled the odor of rue's volatile oil. Women ate the leaves as a contraceptive. However, because rue can cause a rash that is difficult to heal, it fell into disuse and was replaced in cooking, perfume, and medicines by other, less offending herbs.

Shakespeare called rue "the herb of grace." As it was used to get rid of lice and insects, the early Catholic church used rue to repel demons and evil. Rue was reputed to be an antidote to poison, and medieval Europeans classified women as witches if they had rue in their possession. In more modern times rue has been associated with repentance, or "ruefulness."

The FDA approved rue and oil of rue to be used as a flavor component in many major food products, including alcoholic (bitters and vermouth) and nonalcoholic beverages, baked goods, candy, frozen dairy desserts, gelatin, and pudding. Fresh herbs contain a volatile oil used for food flavoring and as an aromatic in perfumes, soaps, and toilet preparations. Rue water, sprinkled about the house, was supposed to kill fleas and repel insects. Rue contains the rule alkaloid arborinine that has anti-inflam-

Rue was reputed to be an antidote to poison, and medieval Europeans classified women as witches if they had rue in their possession.

matory and antihistaminic properties. Rue also contains three elements (furocoumarins, bergapten, and xanthotoxin) that have antispasmodic effects on smooth muscles and have sunblocking properties useful in treating psoriasis. Rutin, the first phytochemical isolated from rue, is best known for its ability to strengthen capillaries and facilitate their ability to transfer fluids. Experiments with rutin have been expanded to include cancer research. In experiments with mice rutin has inhibited tumor formation on the skin and protected skin from irradiation damage. Rutin may be useful for stroke prevention, but more research is needed.

WARNING

The essential oil is considered toxic and can cause death.

FOLKLORE

Ethiopeans grind rue fruit up in a pepper sauce. They also make a cheese, adding the washed leaves to sour milk. Rue leaves are infused with coffee berries to make a beverage.

Arabs add rue to water or chew the leaves to prevent any ill effects of water drunk from strange places.

In Indochina, rue is prescribed for dropsy, neuralgia, rheumatism, fainting spells, and tetanus with the caveat that it should not be given to pregnant women or the chronically ill.

Italians eat rue in salads because it is said to preserve eyesight.

Juice from rue relieves earaches.

Rue was used to ward off the evil eye.

Rue is used medicinally as bitters, or an aromatic appetite stimulant, and an antispasmodic. Rue either stimulates the menstrual flow or suppresses the onset of the menses. It also relieves pain from gas and colic and treats epilepsy, hysteria, and menopause.

Rue was said to heal snakebites and the stings of bees, scorpions, and wasps.

Rue leaf is said to remedy tumors of the uterus, cancer of the mouth, and warts.

Rue seeds are said to be a remedy for warts and tumors.

Rue is said to prevent dizziness, epilepsy, eye inflammations, and insanity.

In Iran, rue is mixed with ground acorns and applied for itch relief.

The Algerians mixed the powdered rue seeds with honey to treat spleen ailments; they used the leaves for fever, fumigation, and syphilis.

The Lebanese used rue for colds and colic as well as arthritis, bruises, rheumatism, and sciatica.

The Syrians used rue in lotions for mumps and skin disorders.

Punjabis use the rue leaves to relieve rheumatic pain.

Saffron

Crocus sativus L.

Thy plants are an orchard of pomegranates, with pleasant fruits; camphire,
with spikenard, spikenard and saffron; calamus and cinnamon, with every
kind of incense tree, with myrrh and aloes and the finest spices.

Song of Solomon 4:13–14

POSSIBLE BENEFITS

Cancer	Measles
Chickenpox	Mumps
Contagious respiratory infections	Painful menstruation

Solomon filled his garden with exotic plants and herbs that pleased the senses and enhanced sensuality. In biblical times saffron was important to people of the East as a condiment and sweet perfume, the stigmas being particularly valued for their food-coloring property. Pliny records that the benches of the public theaters were strewn with saffron, and the costly petals were placed in small fountains to diffuse their scent into public halls.

The crocus in our yards and gardens is slightly different from the saffron crocus in Solomon's garden. The saffron crocus provides seasoning, yellow dye, incense, and medicine obtained from its three stigmas. It is the world's most expensive spice because it takes 4,300 flowers to make an ounce of saffron. Approximately 100,000 flowers yield 1 kilogram of saffron dye.

Many Jews in the Middle Ages were spice merchants, often called "saffron merchants." Their hands and clothes were dyed yellow from weighing out the saffron. Through the ages the yellow color of the spice has been used to mock Jews. Nazi Germany forced Jews to wear the

Crocus sativus L.

yellow Star of David on their clothes to physically distinguish them from the German Aryans.

Saffron is a coloring agent that adds flavor and aroma to rice and meat dishes and confections. It is also used in cosmetics, incense, perfumes, and deodorant. Dissolved in water saffron is used as an ink applied to foreheads on religious and ceremonial occasions. Dioscorides mentions its use as a perfume.

In Europe saffron is used both as a flavoring and as a coloring ingredient; it is a key seasoning in Spanish paella, giving the dish a distinctive yellow appearance. In India, saffron adds yellow shades to curry, and druggists add it to medicines.

Medicinally the plant was used to prepare tinctures for gastric and intestinal remedies and as an antiflatulent. Saffron often is cited as a folk remedy for various types of cancers (tumors of the abdomen, bladder, kidney, liver, neck, spleen, stomach, and uterus, as well as cancers of the breast, mouth, ear, eye and tonsils). Saffron is used to promote eruption of measles. In small doses it is considered to be antispasmodic, expectorant, sedative, and a stimulant.

Some Indian medical formulae still include saffron. It's sometimes used to promote menstruation and is regarded as useful for bladder, kidney, and liver ailments as well as for cholera. Mixed with ghee, it's used to treat diabetes. Saffron oil is rubbed on the belly when uterine sores are suspected. In ancient herbals,

It is the world's most expensive spice because it takes 4,300 flowers to make an ounce of saffron.

an extract of saffron was used to relieve spasms, increase menstrual blood flow, and as a general stimulant.

WARNING

Overdoses of saffron are narcotic. Ten grams of saffron can be a lethal dose. Five grams can induce hemorrhaging. No risk is known at 1.5 grams. The corms are toxic to young animals.

FOLKLORE

The Lebanese add a dozen saffron crocus stigmas to a large cup of hot water for children coming down with chickenpox, measles, or mumps. The tea is considered antiseptic and tonic and to relieve spasms.

Algerians and gypsies use the saffron infusion as a eyewash. Eight to ten filaments or stigmas of the drug per cup of tea is used "as a narcotic for cases of asthma, whooping cough, and hysteria."

Sodom Apple

Solamon incanum L.

The way of the lazy is overgrown with thorns, but the path of the upright is a level highway.

Proverbs 15:19

POSSIBLE BENEFITS

Cancer	*Pleurisy*
Dermatitis	*Sore throat*
Melanoma	*Toothaches*

CAUTION

Poisonous

In the Bible, thorns, briers or briars, and thistles tear at the body and clothes as sin tears at the soul. They impede progress along the road if one strays from the straight and narrow. The Sodom apple, or gray nightshade, may be one of the biblical briars or thorns. Today the bush is limited to the lower Jordan River and Dead Sea areas.

The green, unripe fruits or "apples" are eaten raw or cut into pieces and added to soups as a vegetable. The pieces also can be dried for later use. The fruits and seeds are used as a cheese rennet in both West Africa and East Asia. Juice from the Sodom apple was used as a component in love potions. Although the leaves are edible, Sodom apple is not used as a potherb. Bushmen use the fruit juice from the Sodom apple in arrow poisons.

Sodom apples are reported to "cure" carcinoma and melanoma. The Sodom apple is closely related to the eggplant that contains the alkaloids used in the new Australian drug Curaderm™. The drug reportedly cleared (showed no incidence of) twenty-eight patients with basal cell carcinoma, twenty with squamous cell carcinoma, and twenty-four with keratosis. Curaderm looks promising, but more research with larger numbers of subjects is necessary before any sound conclusions can be drawn. Some Australians claim the lowest concentration of ointment was applied to the growing part of a skin cancer at its deepest edge. Curaderm healed the surface cancer while, underneath, the deepest part of the cancer might still grow and grow more rapidly, at that.

FOLKLORE

The women from the Paniya tribe take Sodom apple as an oral contraceptive.

Sodom apples are used as a remedy for toothache and for sore throat. A decoction of the leaves is taken to relieve chest disorders (pleurisy, pneumonia).

Ethiopians use the Sodom apple leaf for bloat and nosebleeds; the fruit for constipation, gonorrhea, itch, and wounds; the root for gonorrhea; and the ash for scabies.

Conversely, the Sodom apple is a fertility symbol for barren Nigerian women.

In Lesotho Sodom apple fruit is used for sore throat and toothaches.

A poultice or infusion of the fruit from the Sodom apple is applied to external benign tumors.

Tanzanians take the root of the Sodom apple for abdominal pain, carbuncles, and liver disease; the fruit for snakebite; the gall for earaches.

South Africans of Europeans descent use the fruit juice from Sodom apples to eliminate dandruff.

The root of the Sodom apple plant is used as medicine for horses.

Zulus use the juice from the Sodom apple plant for ringworm.

Spikenard

Nardostachys grandiflora DC or *N. jatamansi*

While he was at Bethany in the house of Simon the leper, as he sat at the table, a woman came with an alabaster jar of very costly ointment of nard, and she broke open the jar and poured the ointment on his head.

Mark 14:3

POSSIBLE BENEFITS

Chorea	*Insomnia*
Cramps	*Irregular heartbeat*
Epilepsy	*Leprosy*
Headaches	*Painful menstruation*
Heart disease	

CAUTION

Toxic

Twice in the New Testament Jesus is anointed with nard—once on his head and once on his feet. During his visit with Simon, the woman of the streets anointed Jesus with one of the costliest perfumes of ancient Israel. Winifred Walker, in her book *All the Plants of the Bible*, explains that spikenard was carried in alabaster boxes to preserve the volatile essential oil. It was a very expensive perfume: one pound cost 300 denarii; one denarii equaled a day's pay for a laborer in Jesus' time. The woman's extravagance left everyone stunned, wondering how she could afford such a luxury.

Spikenard, or nard, is an aromatic plant from which is extracted a highly prized essential oil or perfume. Spikenard was imported from the mountains of India, where its rhizomes were used as a drug and in perfumery. The entire plant may be used for its aromatic

Nardostachys grandiflora DC

oils as cosmetics and perfume. Medicinally it was prescribed as a stimulant.

One ancient story concerns Alexander the Great. While riding an elephant along the border of Egypt around 332 BC, his elephant trod over a patch of nard. Alexander became intoxicated by one whiff of the fragrance, similar to that of citronella. Modern day citronella is derived from lemon grasses growing in Southeast Asia. Nard was noted for its unique aroma as late as 1851 AD when it was exhibited in London's Crystal Palace in Kew Gardens.

The spikenard rhizome contains the compound jatamansi, a component in the drug jatamansone. It is reported to promote the growth of hair and blacken hair color. The root extracts show sedative properties. An infusion made from spikenard rhizomes is reported to be useful in treating epilepsy, hysteria, heart palpitations, and chorea. The nard tincture is given for intestinal colic and flatulence. Spikenard oil possesses an anti-arrhythmic activity, possibly therapeutic in treating auricular flutter. Jatamansone is more potent than the spikenard oil and more active than quinine in ventricular rapid heart rate resulting from acute myocardial infarction.

Jatamansone possesses sedative and anti-convulsant action as well. The spikenard oil exerts a hypotensive effect. In moderate doses, it has a distinct depressant action on the central nervous system and relaxes the skeletal and soft tissue muscles. Lethal doses cause deep narcosis and death within a few hours.

Skin-Friendly Bug Juice

Colleen Smith, Special to
The Denver Post

13 *drops of lemon eucalyptus* (Eucalyptus citriodoras) *oil*

13 *drops lavender oil*

10 *drops rosemary oil*

7 *drops citronella oil*

1 *drop clove oil*

Add essential oils to either 2 ounces of witch hazel for a spray-on formula, or to 1 ounce of hazelnut oil to be applied at pulse points. If you substitute regular eucalyptus oil for lemon eucalyptus oil, either increase the citronella oil by two drops or add one to two drops of essential lemon oil. Apply essential oil-based insect repellents frequently.

Caution: Lemon oil can burn the skin.

Today citronella, an effective fragrance in discouraging mosquitoes and flies, is reminesent of that of spikenard. The essential oil of citronella is expressed from lemon grasses from Southeast Asia. Many commercial brands are available on the market, but they often stain clothes or produce skin rashes among individuals highly sensitive to citronella's properties. You might find the recipe on page 212 effective at repelling insects while user-friendly to your skin (if you're not allergic to any of the ingredients). It will also give you a whiff of the highly aromatic but expensive spikenard.

FOLKLORE

In Iran spikenard root tea is used for cardiac and nervous disorders.

Spikenard has a folk reputation for helping cancerous ailments.

Ayurvedics use the spikenard roots to treat bad complexion, biliousness, blood disorders, burning sensation, erysipelas, fever, leprosy, skin ailments, throat disorders, and ulcers.

Storax (Stacte)

Styrax officinalis

Take unto thee sweet spices, stacte, and onycha, and galbanum;
these sweet spices with pure frankincense: of each shall there be a like weight:
And thou shalt make it a perfume.

Exodus 30:34

POSSIBLE BENEFITS

Arthritis	*Hysteria*
Bronchitis	*Low sperm count*
Cancer	*Sores*
Cold	

The Hebrew word *nataph* for gums and resins means "a liquid drop." The drops of resin from the storax or stacte shrubs are collected and hardened either into compressed masses or in smaller drops called *tears*. Storax gum and benzoin gum are closely related.

The storax tree originated in Mediterranean countries. The gum was traded throughout Asia and the Middle East long before the birth of Christ. The gum was used in the preparation of medicines, particularly in cough mixtures and ointments for rheumatism. It was also widely used in the perfume industry.

Approved for food use by the FDA, benzoin gum is customarily used in alcoholic beverages. Benzoin adds the gloss to chocolate eggs, the turgidity to syrups, and some of the flavor to baked goods, candies, chewing gums, gelatins, ice creams, puddings, and soft drinks.

Benzoin is valued as an antioxidant and antiseptic. Perhaps its most important pharmaceutics role is in Compound Benzoin Tincture™, which also contains aloe and balsam, used for cold sores and cracked skin. Also, benzoin is used as an incense, either by itself or combined with other aromatic substances, becoming one of many of the forms of frank-incense.

Warning

Benzoin is regarded as moderately toxic. Heated benzoin gives off a white vapor which may induce coughing and a powdered resin that may induce sneezing.

Folklore

An ointment made from benzoin gum,

called "virgins milk," has been used to heal cracked nipples and vaginal infections.

Benzoin vapors are an expectorant and the tincture of stacte is antiseptic.

Malayans use storax gum for cracked feet and circumcisions.

Tragacanth

Astragalus gummifer Labill.

Then their father Israel said to them, "If it must be so, then do this: take some of the choice fruits of the land in your bags, and carry them down as a present to the man a little balm and a little honey, gum, myrrh, pistachio nuts, and almonds."

Genesis 43:11

POSSIBLE BENEFITS

Burns   *Cough*

Cancer   *Diarrhea*

In the Bible *tragacanth* appears to be translated alternately as either spice or gum. In reality it is a gum and one of the oldest natural emulsifiers known to man. It is a member of the astragalus genus. The desert astragal is native to Palestine and grows equally well at 9,000 feet above sea level or on the shores of the Dead Sea at 1,292 feet below sea level. The gum exudes from several spiny shrubs of the astragal family in several countries in the Middle East. In the Bible *nekhoth*, carried from Gilead with other resins and fruits, may well have been tragacanth gum. *Nekhoth* is very similar to the Arabic words for tragacanth, *nakaa* or *nakaath*.

Tragacanth gum, once used to stiffen calico and crepe, is extensively used in

In reality it is a gum and one of the oldest natural emulsifiers known to man.

216

vaginal jellies and creams, low-calorie syrups, toothpastes, and hand lotions. The gum is used in salad dressings, sauces, ice creams, confections, syrups, milk powder stabilizers, citrus oil emulsions, and cheeses. In Iran, one of the sources of high-grade tragacanth, it is largely used in medicine and confectionery.

Observational data indicates that tragacanth strongly inhibits cancer cells. However, more medical research is needed to back up these observations. Tragacanth is occasionally used as a remedy for burns, coughs, or diarrhea, where demulcents are indicated.

FOLKLORE

The Lebanese dry and powder tragacanth gum to sprinkle on cuts and wounds.

Turmeric

Curcuma longa L.

[N]ard and saffron, calamus and cinnamon, with all trees of frankincense, myrrh and aloes, with all chief spices—a garden fountain, a well of living water, and flowing streams from Lebanon.

Song of Solomon 4:14–15

POSSIBLE BENEFITS

Anti-inflammatory	*Dyspepsia*
Antiflatulence	*Expectorant*
Arthritis	*Laryngitis*
Bronchitis	*Lymphoma*
Diuretic	*Rheumatism*

Okay. I confess. I *want* turmeric to be the saffron mentioned in the Bible. It's such a *good* herb that it *deserves* to be in the Bible. I plead my case as follows:

Dried rhizomes are used as spice, whole or ground, to flavor meat and egg dishes, and to flavor or color pickles, relishes, prepared mustard, butter and cheese; turmeric is an indispensable constituent of curry powder.

Turmeric provides a natural dye to color cloth, leather, silk, palm fiber, wool, and cotton.

As a chemical indicator turmeric changes color in alkaline and acid substrates. Turmeric paper, prepared by soaking unglazed white paper in the tincture and then drying it, is used as a test for alkaloids and boric acid.

Turmeric rhizomes yield an orange-yellow essential oil used in flavoring spice products and in perfumery.

Powdered turmeric is antioxidant.

Curcuma longa L.

The essential oil of turmeric contains curcumin and has shown antiarthritic and anti-inflammatory activity in rats.

Three plants vie for the honor of being the biblical saffron: the saffron crocus, turmeric, and safflower. Since saffron is mentioned only once in the Bible, this plant presents a conundrum for botanists. Each of the plant candidates has its supporters and detractors. Linguistically, the issue is the proper translation and interpretation of the Hebrew *kakom* and the Arabic *kurkum* or *saferam*. Botanically, the three candidate plants differ widely. Crocus grow short flowers from a corm; the scent, seasoning, medicine, and yellow dye are produced by the three stigmas. Turmeric grows tall from a rhizome; the root or rhizome is the source of essential oil, seasoning, medicine, and yellow dye. Safflower grows tall from roots; the flowers produce the fragrance and yellow dye, but neither seasoning nor medicine. Historically, the saffron crocus was probably indigenous to Greece and Asia Minor. It was imported to ancient Israel. Turmeric was indigenous to the Far East and also imported to Palestine and cultivated there in post-biblical times. Safflower was indigenous to Asia Minor and Iran. All three were introduced to cultivation throughout the Mediterranean area and Europe.

I am sure that humans have used saffron and turmeric for thousands of years. And I believe that turmeric as a pain reliever has preceded aspirin by 2,000 years. And like the new miracle aspirins of 1999 (Celebrex and Vioxx) and the millennium aspirin, a COX-2 (cyclooxygenase) inhibitor, turmeric is easier on the tummy as it relieves biblical aches and pains.

FOLKLORE

Medicinally turmeric, taken internally, is regarded as a cure for liver and ulcer troubles. Applied externally as an ointment it heals skin sores.

Asians use the turmeric rhizome for jaundice. Individual research claims that turmeric possesses liver-cleansing qualities.

Ayurvedics use the essential turmeric oil

as an antiseptic, antacid, apéritif, and tonic in small doses and as relief for spasms in larger doses

Boiled with milk and sugar is used as a cold remedy.

Turmeric is given to stop diarrhea.

Indians apply the turmeric root to leech bites. Inhaling fumes from burning turmeric relieves nasal congestion.

The turmeric root, parched and powdered,

relieves bronchitis. A paste made from fresh turmeric rhizome is applied to the head to counteract attacks of vertigo.

Cambodians apply turmeric leaves to reduce fevers.

Turmeric and alum are blown into the ear to relieve infections. A paste of the flowers is used to cure ringworm, other parasitic skin diseases, and gonorrhea.

In Madagascar, the turmeric rhizome is used as a mild laxative, astringent, anti-flatulent, detergent, diuretic, stimulant, and tonic.

Walnut

Juglans regia L.

I went down into the garden of nuts to see the fruits of the valley, and to see whether the vine flourished, and the pomegranates budded.

Song of Solomon 6:11

POSSIBLE BENEFITS

Baldness	*Gingivitis*
Cancer	*Halitosis*
Flu	*Headaches*

One of King Solomon's most valuable fruit trees was the walnut, a handsome tree with smooth gray bark and fresh green leaves. Walnuts were widely cultivated in biblical times for the nuts and timber. Greeks and Romans regarded walnuts as symbols of fertility. The Greeks offered walnuts to their goddess Artemis; Romans scattered walnuts among the guests at weddings.

In Jesus' time, walnut trees grew on the shores of the Sea of Galilee. If Jesus' seamless coat was a rich dark brown, the dye may have come from the thick, heavy green rind encasing the walnut shell. Walnut bark produces a red dye for coloring the lips for cosmetic purposes. Walnuts are also used to tint gray hair black. The outer fleshy part of the fruit produces a yellow dye.

The walnut is 50 percent oil. When dry pressed, the nuts yield a valuable oil used in paints and soaps. When cold pressed, they yield a light yellow edible oil used for flavoring, cooking, and lighting.

In some countries walnut bark is used as a toothbrush. Its extract shows broad-spectrum antimicrobial activity, inhibiting growth of several species of pathogenic micro-organisms (*Staphylococcus aureous* and *Streptococcus mutans*, *Escherichia coli*, and *Pseudomonas aeruginosa*) and a pathogenic yeast (*Candida albicans*). Thus, brushing the teeth with this bark may improve oral hygiene, prevent plaque and caries formation, and reduce the incidence of gingival and periodontal infections.

Despite the fact that

nuts are high in fat,

research confirms that

a high intake of nuts

is associated with a

reduced risk profile for

cardiovascular disease.

With walnut's anticancer folk history, research has found that walnut contains the antitumor compound, juglone. Juglone also shows some pesticidal attributes.

Walnuts are one of the greatest sources of serotonin, and serotonin controls hunger. The nuts also contain dietary tryptophan that converts to cerebral serotonin. Eating walnuts and pecans alleviates hunger and might prevent overeating. Despite the fact that nuts are high in fat, research confirms that a high intake of nuts is associated with a reduced risk profile for cardiovascular disease. Serotonin also stimulates nitric oxide that relaxes the smooth muscle cells, reduces platelet aggregation and adhesion in the blood, diminishes low oxidation of low-density lipoprotein (LDLs), and relaxes blood vessels. Thus, walnuts may lower blood pressure and aid relaxation. Red grape skins (as well as Concord grape juice and Cabernet Sauvignon) have the same beneficial effects as walnuts. If you want more fiber than Concord grape juice or Cabernet Sauvignon provides, try a Waldorf salad. Watch your allergies and adapt the ingredients accordingly.

FOLKLORE

Asians use walnut kernels to treat laryngeal and lung disorder and mix them with almond and ginseng for chronic coughs; the oil is used for skin ailments.

The Chinese use walnut leaves and powdered hulls as an astringent and cleansing agent for syphilis.

The Lebanese believe the walnut increases fertility.

The Lebanese use walnut husks as an anodyne.

Algerians burned the walnut shells in sugar for headaches.

North Africans inhaled the smoke of burning walnut shells for nasal inflammation and influenza.

In Algeria, the leaf decoction is used as a shampoo to prevent baldness.

The green walnut husk was utilized medicinally as a laxative.

Waldorf Salad

Diced red apples (e.g., Macintosh, Jonathan, red delicious)

Handfuls of nuts (almonds, walnuts, pecans)

One or two bunches of red grapes (halved)

One or two handfuls of raisins

Toss with oil or mayonnaise of choice. Squeeze some lemon juice over the mixture and serve with a bean casserole loaded with garlic and onions. Sip one glass of red wine or a cinnamon-cranberry juice cocktail, chilled or over ice. Don't you feel better already?

A decoction of crushed walnut leaves was used as an insect repellent and as a tea.

Walnut leaves were prescribed as an astringent.

Watercress

Nasturtium officinale R. Bn.

Now before the festival of the Passover, Jesus knew that his hour
had come to depart from this world and go to the Father. Having loved
his own who were in the world, he loved them to the end.

John 13:1

POSSIBLE BENEFITS

Asthma	*Dermatitis*
Cancer	*Kidney infection*
Cold	*Tuberculosis*

Watercress may be one of the bitter herbs of the Passover (along with chicory, endive, and lettuce). During the Exodus from Egypt, the Jews collected several herbs during their trip through the desert. Since we cannot be certain which of the plants now used were those collected, we list them collectively under bitter herbs. In the Holy Land they grow wild along the banks of streams and rivers.

We cannot be absolutely sure which among the bitter herbs are truly those of the Bible. Lettuce and endives have lost the bitter taste of the wild varieties through development and selection. What else other

Watercress, is still sought after for its pungent leaves and tender young stems

than bitterness has been lost can only be speculated. Watercress, however, is still sought after for its pungent leaves and tender young stems; the sharp flavor is due to gluconasturtin. Watercress is used widely for garnishing meats, salads and other dishes, even biscuits. The plant is fairly high in vitamins, minerals and protein. As a salad, it can stimulate the appetite.

FOLKLORE

The Lebanese apply bruised watercress leaves mixed with yogurt to free the face of acne, blemishes, blotches, and spots. The juice, mixed with egg whites, is said to help carcinoma. Made into snuff, it is a "cure" for polyps.

Watercress juice is antibacterial and relieves asthma, dry throats, head colds, and tuberculosis.

The watercress plant is said to be an antidote to nicotine poisoning and useful in relieving urinary tract and goiter disorders.

Cress in vinegar is one remedy for anthrax.

In China, the watercress plant is used for asthma.

Stuffing pillows with watercress leaves is supposed to induce sleep.

In Western Europe, watercress is used to ease menstruation. It is believed to interfere with implantation of the ovum and may act as an oral contraceptive.

Watercress is used as a blood-cleanser and for kidney ailments.

227

In Africa chopped watercress, covered with honey overnight, is used as a cough syrup.

The pungent compounds (isothi-ocyantes) may have cancer preventive properties.

Watermelon

Citrullus lanatus Thunb.

We remember the fish, which we did eat in Egypt freely; the cucumbers, and the melons.

Numbers 11:5

POSSIBLE BENEFITS

Cystitis	*Gonorrhea*
Dyspepsia	*Prostate disorder*
Fever	

Watermelons, melons, muskmelons, or cucumbers are all candidates for the biblical melon. They all contain 90 percent water, which made them invaluable and highly desirable while traveling or living in the desert. Only the degree of sweetness separates the varieties. Watermelons were grown in Egypt and ancient Israel, serving as food, drink, and medicine. Salted and roasted watermelon seeds are still a popular Egyptian side dish today. The fruit and seeds are eaten raw. Oil can be pressed from the seeds and used in salads and cooking. Medi-cinally, the fruit was used as an antiseptic and laxative.

In the old *Materia Medica*, the so-called "Four Greater Cold Seeds" were those of watermelon, pumpkin, gourd, and cucumber. They were bruised and rubbed in water to form an emulsion used to treat throat and sinus inflammations, dyspepsia, fever, and urinary disorders.

Watermelon is eaten chiefly as a fresh fruit. The rind can be made into preserves; the juice can be made into syrup. Watermelon fruit juice is a cooling and refreshing beverage. The seeds may be dried or parched to chew like sunflower seeds, used as a coffee substitute, or ground into flour and baked into bread. Oil extracted from the seeds is used in cooking and lamps. The oil is also rich in the enzyme urease. The fruit is a source of

Citrullus lanatus Thunb.

vitamin A. Watermelon seeds are one of the better sources of phenylalanine, an essential amino acid.

FOLKLORE

Watermelon juice is an antiseptic in typhus fever.

The Lebanese use a decoction of watermelon leaves to lower fevers and flush the kidneys.

In parts of Iran and Iraq, for two months of the year, watermelon, with a little bread, is the peoples' food.

In Lesotho and Tanzania, watermelon leaves are consumed as a vegetable.

West Africa's Yoruba boil the diced watermelon fruit with onion and other roots to treat gonorrhea and milky vaginal discharge.

Tonkinese used the pericarp of watermelon fruit for diarrhea.

In many cultures, the seeds are prescribed for urinary ailments.

In Guyana, watermelon pulp is used as a cooling enema.

In China, watermelon rind is powdered, burned to ashes, and applied to mouth sores.

Crude extract from watermelon seeds lowers the blood pressure.

Ayurvedics consider green watermelon fruit astringent, aphrodisiac, and a fever reducer; the leaves increase hemoglobin in the blood.

Ripe watermelon flesh is eaten as a diuretic and tonic and helps dispel flatulence and alleviate bronchitis and pulmonary catarrh.

In the Bahamas a decoction of bruised and boiled watermelon seeds is drunk as a diuretic.

Expressed liquid from fresh watermelon seeds is used as a dewormer.

In Curaçao, the thick watermelon rind is bound around the forehead to relieve headaches.

In Venezuela, watermelon rind is mashed and applied as a poultice for liver trouble.

In Mexico, a decoction of watermelon leaves is given to malaria patients.

In Tanzania, juice from watermelon leaves is given to malaria patients.

Wheat

Triticum aestivum L.

For the Lord thy God bringeth thee into a good land, a land of
brooks of water, of fountains, and depths that spring out of valleys and hills;
A land of wheat, and barley, and vines, and fig-trees, and pomegranates,
a land of olive-oil, and honey.

Deuteronomy 8:7–8

POSSIBLE BENEFITS

Cancer   Heart disease
Diverticulitis

Wheat is one of the seven plants God promised the Israelites when they reached the Promised Land. It was used in ritual, in export trade, and was consumed as food. The first wheat harvest was a temple offering at Pentecost. (*Pentecost* is a Greek word meaning "the holiday of fifty days" because it was the fiftieth day after the first day of Passover.) Christians celebrate Pentecost on the seventh Sunday after Easter to commemorate the descent of the Holy Spirit on the apostles. In biblical times the parched or toasted grain was consumed or used as a meal offering; flour for bread as well as starch and beer were prepared from the grain.

Wheat starch was used medicinally as an emollient. Wheat germ is an oil expressed from the kernel of the wheat berry. The oil and kernel are high in vitamin E and the B vitamins as well as trace minerals and calcium, magnesium, and phosphorus. Wheat bran is five times higher in fiber than wheat flour. It is a key element in a high-fiber diet that fights cancer and heart disease.

FOLKLORE

In Cornwall the Cornish weave wheat into Celtic designs to hang over doorways. They are thought to protect the room or home against evil spirits

Wheat stalks were used as fodder, animal bedding, compost, mulch, and fertilizer.

Wheat stalks were also woven into hats, baskets, chair seats, and beehives.

Willow

Salix alba L.

On the willows there we hung up our harps. For there our captors asked us for songs, and our tormentors asked for mirth, saying, "Sing us one of the songs of Zion!"

Psalm 137:2–3

POSSIBLE BENEFITS

Cancer	*Milky vaginal discharge*
Colds	*Pain*
Headaches	

The boughs from the willow are among the four species for the Feast of Sukkot: citron and figs and boughs of palms and willow. Willows are graceful, fast-growing trees. They prefer moist places along streambeds, or wadis, where they are useful for holding the banks against seasonal flooding. Willow branches hang low, as if weighted down by other objects, as the allusion in the Psalms to the harps of the captive Israelites suggests.

The wood was used for simple objects like troughs, sieves, tool handles, and small boats and was likely used for fuel. The bark was an ingredient in tanning. Medicinally, salicin, a bitter principle extracted from the bark of young willow shoots, makes a good substitute for quinine. Also, slender willow twigs, or withes, were used in wicker work or woven into baskets and twine. The galls on the leaves contained a dye used on delicate fabrics for veils. The seeds were fabricated into an inferior grade of lamp wick.

The Lebanese recognize the aspirin-like quality of a decoction made from willow bark. They use it for colds, grippe, and pain. A stronger decoction treats venereal disease. Even "transplanted" to America, the Lebanese continue to use the bark of the American willow species for colds, flu, headache, pains,

Salix alba L.

and rheumatism. The leaves are brewed into a tea that is calming and reduces muscle spasms. Willow is the herbalist's aspirin. Tannin and gallic acid might explain its anti-cancer activity. A saccharine manna-like secretion from willows has been recommended for thrush.

In India, willow leaves and bark are considered tonic and used in intermittent and remittent fevers.

Willow catkins and young twigs have been used externally as a poultice for sores.

FOLKLORE

Young willow leaves and branches are used for popular medicine in Palestine.

An infusion of willow leaf is useful for relieving pain of rheumatism.

Wormwood

Artemisia herba-alba Asso

The third angel blew his trumpet, and a great star fell from heaven, blazing like a torch, and it fell on a third of the rivers and on the springs of water. The name of the star is Wormwood. A third of the waters became wormwood, and many died from the water, because it was made bitter.

Revelation 8:10–11

POSSIBLE BENEFITS

Bronchitis	*Fever*
Cold	*Toothache*
Cough	*Worms*

CAUTION

Toxic

The toxic potential of wormwood is obvious from the passage from Revelations. A branch called *Absinthes* or wormwood, fell from the sky like "a great star blazing" into the water so that people died from drinking there. Wormwood has a very bitter taste, which is why some believe wormwood is the bitter gall mentioned in the Bible.

Various species of wormwood were common in ancient Palestine and in the Sinai. Whether one or more of these species qualifies for the biblical wormwood is still undetermined. Bedouins sell several species in the Cairo market today. The drink absinthe is made from a wormwood species, and thousands of gallons were once consumed annually, especially in France. At first the drink incites activity accompanied by pleasant sensations. Absinthe inspires the mind with grandiose ideas illustrating the biblical phrase "he hath made me drunken with wormwood." Most often wormwood is used in a symbolic or medicinal sense; essential oil from wormwood can repel insects and mask offensive odors.

Tea made from dried wormwood leaves is used for gastrointestinal cramps. Wormwood leaves contain the phytochemical moxibustion whose properties seem effective against bronchitis, asthma, and other upper-respiratory ailments. This treatment is found also in Asian and Native American cultures. Bedouins place wormwood leaves inside the nostrils as a nasal decongestant for colds. For coughs they drink a tea made of leaves boiled in water or milk. Bedouins expose their newborn children to the smoke of the burning wormwood leaves to insure the babies' good health.

FOLKLORE

Palestinians use wormwood leaves as a folk remedy for toothaches.

In Egypt wormwood is used against tapeworms.

Bedouins believe that the fumes from the burning wormwood leaves will keep away the evil eye. They use dry woolly galls from wormwoods for tinder to ignite fire with flint stone.

Nile valley farmers fumigate their poultry with the smoke of the burning wormwood leaves and hang out the branches as a snake repellent.

Camels that graze on wormwood are said to be spared certain skin diseases.

Wormwood has been recommended as a forage plant on the high plateau of Algeria.

Taxonomic List of Biblical Herbs

English	Latin	Hebrew	Greek	Arabic
almonds	*Prunus dulcis* (Mill.)	*shaqed*		*louz* or *loz* or *lauz*
aloes	*Aloe vera* (L.) Burm. f.	*ehht*	*aloe*	*musabar*
apples (apricots)	*Prunus armeniaca* L.	*tapuach*		*binkuk*
barley	*Hordeum vulgare* L.	*seorah*	*krithe*	*shaair*
bay laurel	*Laurus nobilis* L.	*ezrach*		*rand*
black cumin	*Nigella sativa* L.	*ketzah*		*habbatussada* or *habba sooda*
black mulberry	*Morus alba* L.	*shekmah*	*sukaminos*	*tuth*
black mustard	*Brassica nigra* L.		*sinapi*	*khardal*
bottle gourd (calabash)	*Lagenaria siceraria* Molina			*karehulmar*
butcher's broom	*Ruscus aculeatus* L.	*rothem*		*khizana*
caper	*Capparis spinosa* L.	*abiyonah*		*kabbar* or *lasafa*
carob	*Ceratonia siliqua* L.	*keration*		*kharrub*
castor bean	*Ricinus communis* L.	*qiqaupm* or *kikayon*		*el keroa* or *kherwa'* or *khirwa*
chicory	*Cichorium intybus* L.	*maror*		*seris*
cinnamon	*Cinnamomum verum* J. Presl or *C. zeylanicum* Blume	*keenamon*		*darsini*
citron	*Citrus medica* L.	*etrog*		*utraj*

English	Latin	Hebrew	Greek	Arabic
coriander (cilantro)	*Coriandrum sativum* L.	*gad*		*kusbara*
cucumber	*Cucumis sativus* L.	*keshuem*		*kheyar*
cumin	*Cuminum cyminum* (L.) or *Cuminum odorum* Salisb.	*kammon*		*kemmoun*
dandelion	*Taraxacum officinale* Weber	*maror*		*nakhl*
date palm	*Phoenix dactylifera* L.	*tamar*		
desert date	*Balanites aegyptiaca* (L.) Delile	*tsori*		*lukkum* or *helig*
dill	*Anethum graveolens* L.	*sabtu*	*anethu*	*shibith* or *shibit*
fava bean	*Vicia faba* L.	*pol*		*foul*
fenugreek	*Trigonella foenum-graecum* L.	*chatsar*		*helbah* or *helba*
fig	*Ficus carica* L.	*teanah*		*tine* or *teen*
flax	*Linum usitatissimum* L.	*peshte*		*bontouma* or *hab e kattan* or *sib muma*
frankincense	*Boswellia sacra* Flueck or *B. carteri* Birdw.	*lebonah*		*luban*
garlic	*Allium sativum* L.	*shum*		*thoum*
grape	*Vitis vinifera* L.	*gepen*		*aenaeb* or *anab*
henna	*Lawsonia inermis* (L.) or *Lawsonia alba* Lam.	*kopher*		*alhenna* or *henna*
horsemint	*Mentha longifolia* (L.) Huds.	*heduosmon*		*na'ana*
hyssop	*Origanum syriacum* or *O. aegyptiacum*	*ezov*		
juniper	*Juniperus oxycedrus* L.	*'ar'or*		*taga*
lentil	*Lens culinaris* Medik.	*adasha*		
mandrake	*Mandragora officinarum* L.	*dud* or *duda'em*		
milk thistle	*Silybum marianum* (L.) Gaertn.	*dardar*		*shouk en-nasara*

English	Latin	Hebrew	Greek	Arabic
muskmelon	*Cucumis melo* L.	*qisu im*		*'aggour*
myrrh	*Cistus inanus creticus* *Commiphora erythraea* (Ehrenb.) Engl.	*lot* (Old Testament) *mor* (New Testament)		
myrtle	*Myrtus communis* L.	*hadas*		*mersin* or *yas* or *hadas*
nettle	*Urtica dioica* L.	*charoom*		
olive	*Olea europaea* L.	*zayeet*		*zaytun* or *itm*
onion	*Allium cepa* L.	*batsal*		*bassal*
pomegranate	*Punica granatum* L.	*rimmon*		*romman* or *ruman*
poppy	*Papaver somniferum* L.	*rosh*		*bou en-noum* or *atyun*
rue	*Ruta graveolens* L.	*peganon*		*aruda* or *sadab*
saffron	*Crocus sativus* L.	*karkom*		*kurkum* or *saferam*
sodom apple (gray nightshade)	*Solanum incanum* L.	*chadeq*		*'arsam*
spikenard	*Nardostachys grandiflora* DC. or *N. jatamans*	*inard*	*narkom*	*sumbululaasffir*
storax (stacte)	*Styrax officinalis*	*nataph*		
tragacanth	*Astragalus gummifer* Labill.	*besem*		
turmeric	*Curcuma longa* L.			*kurkum* or *aurukesafur*
walnut (English)	*Juglans regia* L.	*egoz*		*joz*
watercress	*Nasturtium officinale* R.Br.	*maror*		*qurrat el-'ayn*
watermelon	*Citrullus lanatus* Thunb.	*avoteach*		
wheat	*Triticum aestivum* L.	*cheetah*		*burr*
willow	*Salix alba* L.	*tsaftsafah*		*khilaf*
wormwood	*Artemisia herba-alba* Asso	*laehnah*		*shih*

Bibliography

Albert, S. W. *Rueful Death.* New York: Berkley Crime, 1996.

Alon, A. *The Natural History of the Land of the Bible.* Garden City, New York: Doubleday, 1978.

Anchor Bible Dictionary, vol. 2. New York: Doubleday, 1992.

Anderson, A. W. *Plants of the Bible.* New York: Philosophical Library, 1957.

Antonopoulou, S.; C. A. Demopoulos; and N. K. Andrikopoulos. "Lipid separation from *Urtica dioica*: Existence of platelet-activating factor." *Journal of Agricultural and Food Chemistry* 44, 10 (October 1996), 3052–6.

Aranson, T. R.; J. Hebda; and T. Johns. "Use of plants for food and medicine by native peoples of eastern Canada." Canadian Journal of Botany 59 (1981), 2189–325.

Asimov, I. *Asimov's Guide to the Bible.* New York: Avenel's Books, 1981.

Ayensu, E. S. *Medicinal Plants of West Africa.* Algonac, Michigan: Reference Publications, 1978.

Bailey, C.; and A. Danin. "Bedouin Plant Utilization in Sinai and Negev." *Economic Botany* 35, 2 (April–June 1981), 145–62.

Balch, J. F.; and P. A. Balch. *Prescription for Nutritional Healing,* 2nd ed. Garden City Park, New York: Avery Publishing Group, 1997.

Balfour, J. H. *The Plants of the Bible: Trees and Shrubs.* London: T. Nelson & Sons, 1857.

Bisset, N. G. *Herbal Drugs and Phytopharmaceuticals.* Edited and translated by Max Wichtl. Boca Raton, Florida: CRC Press, 1994.

Bloom, M. *Plants in the Bible in Their Natural Surroundings.* Edited and translated by Michael Berlinger. Haifa, Israel: The Department of Education and Culture, 1969.

Bloomfield, H. H. *Healing Anxiety with Herbs.* New York: HarperCollins, 1998.

Blumenthal, M.; W. R. Busse; A. Goldberg; J. Gruenwald; T. Hall; C. W. Riggins; and R. S. Rister (Eds.). *The Complete German Commission E Monographs. Therapeutic Guide to Herbal Medicines.* Austin, Texas: American Botanical Council; Boston: Integrative Medicine Communications, 1998.

Boulos, L. *Medicinal Plants of North Africa.* Algonac, Michigan: Reference Publications, 1983.

Braithewaite, J. *Corporate Crime in the Pharmaceutical Industry.* Boston: Routledge & Kegan Paul, 1984.

Brown, F.; S. R. Driver; and C. A. Briggs. *A Hebrew and English Lexicon of the Old Testament.* Oxford, London: Oxford University and Clarendon Press, 1906, 1951.

Burkill, J. D. *A Dictionary of the Economic Products of the Malay Peninsula,* vol. 2. Kuala Lumpur: Art Printing Works, 1966.

Cadot, P.; A. M. Kochuyt; R. Deman; and E. A. Stevens. "Inhalative occupational and ingestive immediate-type allergy caused by chicory (*Cichorium intybus*)." *Clinical and Experimental Allergy* 26, 8 (1996), 940–4.

Castetter, E. F.; and R. M. Underhill. "Ethnobiological Studies in the American Southwest: II." *The Papago,* Publication The University of New Mexico Bulletin, vol. 4, 3 (1935), 64–5.

Castleman, M. "Spice-Rack Remedies: Turn to Your Kitchen for Health Care," *Herbs for Health* 1, 1 (November/December 1996), 22–9.

Chancellor, J. *The Flowers and the Fruits of the Bible.* New York: Beaufort Books, 1982.

Chithra, V.; and S. Leelamma. "Hypolipidemic effect of coriander seeds (*Coriandrum sativum*): mechanism of action." *Plant Foods for Human Nutrition* 51, 2 (1997), 167–72.

Cunnane and Thompson (Eds.). *Flaxseed in Human Nutrition.* Champaign, Illinois: AOCS Press, 1995.

Curtin, L.S.M. *By the Prophet of the Earth.* Santa Fe, New Mexico: San Vicente Foundation, 1949.

Dalziel, J. M. *The Useful Plants of West Tropical Africa.* London: The Crown Agents for the Colonies, 1937.

D'epiro, N. W. (Ed.). "Herbal Medicine: What Works; What's Safe." *Patient Care* 31, 16 (1997), 48–77.

Densmore, F. "Uses of Plants by the Chippewa Indians," *Publication SI-BAE Annual Report #44*: (1928), 273–379.

De Smet, P.A.G.M.; K. Keller; R. Hansel; and R. F. Chandler (Eds.). *Adverse Effects of Herbal Drugs 3.* Berlin: Springer-Verlag, 1997.

Duke, J. A. *CRC Handbook of Biologically Active Phytochemicals and Their Activities.* Boca Raton, Florida: CRC Press, 1992.

——. *CRC Handbook of Edible Weeds.* Boca Raton, Florida: CRC Press, 1992.

——. *CRC Handbook of Medicinal Herbs.* Boca Raton, Florida: CRC Press, 1985.

——. *CRC Handbook of Phytochemical Constituents in GRAS Herbs and Other Economic Plants.* Boca Raton, Florida: CRC Press, 1992.

——. *The Green Pharmacy.* Emmaus, Pennsylvania: Rodale Press, 1997.

——. *Handbook of Legumes of World Economic Importance.* New York: Plenum Press, 1981.

——. *Handbook of Northeastern Indian Medicinal Plants.* Lincoln, Massachusetts: Quarterman Publications, 1986.

——. "The quest for tolerant germplasm," ASA (Madison, Wisconsin) Special Symposium 32, "Crop tolerance to suboptimal land conditions." *American Society of Agronomy*,1978.

——. "Utilization of Papaver." *Economic Botany* 27, 4 (October–December 1973), 390–1.

——; and E. S. Ayensu. *Medicinal Plants of China,* vol. 2, book No. 4 in the series *Medicinal Plants of the World.* Algonac, Michigan: Reference Publications, 1985.

——; and R. Barnett. "Cole's role," *American Health* 8, 8 (1989), 100, 102.

——; and J. L. duCellier. *CRC Handbook of Alternative Cash Crops.* Boca Raton, Florida: CRC Press, 1993.

——; and P. Duke. *Medicinal Plants of the Bible.* Buffalo, New York: Trado-Medic Books, 1983.

——; and R. Vazquez Martinez. *Amazonian Ethnobotanical Dictionary Peru.* Boca Raton, Florida: CRC Press, 1994.

——; and K. Wain. *Medicinal Plants of the World: Computerized Index.* Economic Botany Laboratory, Beltsville, Maryland: USDA, 1981.

Elmore, F. H. *Ethnobotany of the Navajo.* Santa Fe, New Mexico: Monographs of the School of American Research, 1944.

Fernald, M. L.; A. C. Kinsey; and R. C. Rollins. *Edible Wild Plants of Eastern North America,* rev. ed. New York: Harper & Bros., 1958.

Fetter, A. T. *Potpourri, Incense and Other Fragrant Concoctions.* New York: Workman, 1977.

Fleming, T. et al. *PDR for Herbal Medicine,* 1st ed. Montvate, New Jersey: Medical Economics, 1998.

Foster, S. *101 Medicinal Herbs.* Loveland, Colorado: Interweave Press, 1998.

——; and J. A. Duke. *A Field Guide to Medicinal Plants: Eastern and Central North America.* "A Peterson Field Guide," Boston, Massachusetts: Houghton Mifflin, 1990.

Ghazanfar, S. A. *Handbook of Arabian Medicinal Plants.* Boca Raton, Florida: CRC Press, 1994.

Gibernau, M.; H. R. Buser; J. E. Frey; and M. Hossaert-McKey. "Volatile compounds from extracts of figs of *Ficus carica*." *Phytochemistry* (Oxford) 46, 2 (February 1997), 241–4.

Gilmer, M. *Rooted in the Spirit: Exploring Inspirational Gardens.* Dallas, Texas: Taylor Publishing, 1997.

Grieve, M. *A Modern Herbal,* vols. I & II. New York: Dover Publications, 1971.

Hamel, P.; and M. Chiltoskey. *Cherokee Plants and Their Uses.* Sylva, North Carolina: Herald Publishing, 1975.

Hampton, A. *Natural Organic Hair and Skin Care.* Tampa, Florida: Organica Press, 1987.

The HarperCollins Study Bible: New Revised Standard Version. New York: HarperCollins, 1993.

Hartwell, J. L. *Plants Used Against Cancer: A Survey.* Lincoln, Massachusetts: Quarterman Publications (1967–1971), 30–4.

Hernandez Mesa, M. *Las Plantas Biblicas. Sus Propiedades Medicinales y su Applicacion Practica por 1 os Sistemas Homeopatico y Natural.* Bogota: undated.

Herrick, J. W. *Iroquois Medical Botany.* Ann Arbor, Michigan: University Microfilms International, 1977.

Hoffmann, David. *The Complete Illustrated Holistic Herbal.* Rockport, Massachusetts: Element Books, 1996.

Holy Bible: King James Version. Wichita, Kansas: Heirloom Bible, 1964.

Jain, S. K.; and R. A. DeFilipps. *Medicinal Plants of India,* vols. 1–2. Algonac, Michigan: Reference Publications, 1991.

James, W. *Gardening with Biblical Plants.* Chicago: Nelson Hall, 1983.

Jansen, P.C.M. "Spices, Condiments, and Medicinal Plants in Ethiopia: Their Taxonomy and Agricultural Significance." *Agricultural Research Reports, 906.* Wageningen, The Netherlands: Center for Agricultural Publishing and Documentation, 1981.

Keshri, G.; V. Lakshmi; and M. M. Singh. "Postcoital contraceptive activity of some indigenous plants in rats." *Contraception* 57, 5 (May 1998), 357–60.

Kim, M.; and H. K. Shin. "The water-soluble extract of chicory reduces glucose uptake from the perfuse jejunum in rats." *Journal of Nutrition* 126, 9 (September 1996), 2236–42.

King, E. A. *Bible Plants for American Gardens.* New York: Dover, 1975.

Kingsbury, J. M. *Poisonous Plants of the United States and Canada.* Englewood Cliffs, New Jersey: Prentice-Hall, 1964.

Kirtikar, K. R.; and B. D. Basu. *Indian Medicinal Plants,* vols. 1–4. Delhi, India: Jayyed Press, 1975.

Kolatch, A. J. *The Jewish Book of Why.* Middle Village, New York: Jonathan David Publishers, 1981.

Kulevanova, S.; and T. Ristov. "The content of minerals in nettle (*Urtica dioica L.*) and nettle extracts." *Acta Pharmacologia Et Taxicologia* (Zagreb) 45, 3 (1995), 481–6.

Laughlin, J. C. "The effect of band placed nitrogen and phosphorus fertilizer on the yield of poppies (*Papaver somniferum L.*) grown in Krasnozem soil." *Acta Horticulturae* 73 (1978), 165–9.

Leung, A. Y. *Encyclopedia of Common Natural Ingredients Used in Foods, Drugs and Cosmetics.* New York: John Wiley & Sons, 1980.

Lininger, S. (Ed.). *The Natural Pharmacy.* Rocklin, California: Prima Publications, 1998.

Loof, B. "Poppy cultivation." *Field Crop Abstracts* 19, 1 (1966), 1–5.

"Magic and Medicine of Plants." *Reader's Digest* Pleasantville, New York (1993).

McGuffin M.; C. Hobbs; R. Upton; and A. Goldberg (Eds.). *American Herbal Products Association's Botanical Safety Handbook.* Boca Raton, Florida: CRC Press.

The Medical Advisor: The Complete Guide to Alternative & Conventional Treatments. Alexandria, Virginia: Time Life, 1996.

Moerman, D. E. *American Medical Ethnobotany. A Reference Dictionary.* New York: Garland Publishing, 1977.

Moldenke, H. N. "The Economic Plants of the Bible." *Economic Botany* 8 (1954), 152–63.

Moldenke, H. N.; and A. L. Moldenke. *Plants of the Bible.* New York: The Ronald Press Co., 1952.

Moss, R. *Herbs against Cancer.* New York: Equinox Press, 1998.

"Natural Health Shopper," May 1998; as quoted in *Natural Pharmacy* 2, 9 (September 1998), 4.

Nelson's Complete Concordance of the Revised Standard Version Bible, 2nd ed. Nashville, Tennessee: Thomas Nelson, 1957.

The New Jerome Biblical Commentary. Englewood Cliffs, New Jersey: Prentice-Hall, 1968, 1990.

Newall, C. A., L. A. Anderson, and J. D. Phillipson. *Herbal Medicine—A Guide for Health-care Professionals.* London: The Pharmaceutical Press, 1996.

Pedersen, M. *Nutritional Herbology: A Reference Guide to Health.* Warsaw, Indiana: Wendell W. Whitman Co., 1998.

Perry, L. M. *Medicinal Plants of East and Southeast Asia.* Cambridge, Massachusetts: MIT Press, 1980.

Philips, H. J. *Some Lebanese Materia Medica: Lebanese Folk Cures,* vol. II. (Ph.D. diss., Anthropology) Columbia University: Microfilms (1957), 457.

Purseglove, J. W.; E. G. Brown; C. L. Green; and S.R.J. Robbins. *Spices,* vols. 1–2. London: Longman, 1981.

Preuss, J. *Medicine in the Bible and Talmud.* Edited and translated by Fred Rosner. New York: Aronson, 1994.

Quillin, P. "The ideal anti-cancer diet." *American Journal of Natural Medicine* 5, 7 (1998), 21–5.

Quisumbing, E. "Medicinal Plants of the Philippines." *Philippine Department of Agriculture & Natural Resources Technical Bulletin* 16 (1951).

Rabinowitz, L. I. *Torah and Flora.* New York: Sanhedrin Press, 1977.

Reed, C. F. *Selected Weeds of the United States, Handbook No. 366,* Washington, D.C.: USDA, 1970.

Roman-Ramos, R.; J. L. Flores-Saenz; and F. J. Alarcon-Aguilar. "Anti-hyperglycemic effect of some edible plants." *Journal of Ethnopharmacology* 48, 1 (1995), 25–32.

Schulz, V.; R. Hansel; and V. E. Tyler. *Rational Phytotherapy: A Physician's Guide to Herbal Medicine,* 3rd ed. Translated by Terry C. Telger, Heidelberg, Germany: Springer Verlag, 1998.

Schilcher, H. *Phytotherapy in Paediatrics: Handbook for Physicians and Pharmacists,* 2nd ed. Translated by A. R. Meus. Stuttgart, Germany: Medical Pharmacy Publications, 1997.

Scully, V. A. *Treasury of American Indian Herbs.* New York: Bonanza Books, 1970.

Serraclara, A., et al. "Hypoglycemic action of an oral fig-leaf decoction in Type-I diabetic patients." *Diabetes Research and Clinical Practice* 30 (1998), 19–22.

Shemluck, M. "Medicinal and other uses of the Compositae by Indians in the United States and Canada." *Journal of Ethnopharmacology* 5 (1982), 303–58.

Shirwaikar, A., et al. "Chemical investigation and anti-hepatotoxic activity of the root bark of *Capparis spinosa.*" *Fitoterapia* 67, 3 (1996), 200–4.

Smit, D. *Plants of the Bible: A Gardener's Guide.* Oxford, England: Lion Publishing, 1992.

Smith, C. "Flax facts: Linen still great." *The Denver Post,* Sunday, July 25, 1999, 6–7F.

———. "Naturally repellent," *The Denver Post,* Sunday, June 20, 1999, 3G.

Smith, G. W. "Arctic Pharmacognosi." *Publication Arctic* 26 (1973), 324–33.

Smith, H. H. "Ethnobotany of the Meskwaki Indians." *Bulletin of the Public Museum of the City of Milwaukee* 4 (1928), 175–326.

———. "Ethnobotany of the Ojibwe Indians." *Publication Bulletin of the Public Museum of the City of Milwaukee* 4 (1932) 327–525.

Speck, F. G., R. B. Hassrick; and E. S. Carpenter. *Rappa-*

hannock Herbals, Folklore and Science of Cures. Proc. Del. County Inst. of Sci., 1942.

Srimal, R. C. "Turmeric: A brief review of medicinal properties." *Fitoterapia* 68, 6 (1997), 483–93.

Tabor's Cyclopedic Medical Dictionary, 16 ed. Philadelphia: E. A. Davis, 1985.

Taniguchi M.; M. Yanai; Y. Qing Xiao; T. Kido; and K. Baba. "Three new isocoumarins from *Coriandrum sativum.*" *Phytochem* 42 (n.d.), 843–6.

Tantaquidgeon, G. C.; G. Lloyd; and C. Westey. "Folk Medicine of the Delaware and Related Algonkian Indians. Mohegan Medicinal Practices. Weather-lore and Superstition. Surviving Folktales & Herbal Lore Among the Shinnecock Indians." *Journal of American Folklore* 58 (1972), 113–23. (Pennsylvania Historical and Museum Commission Authority. Papers #3 SI-BAE Annual Report #43: 264–70.)

Tucker, A. O. *Economic Botany,* vol. 40(4). (October–December 1986), 425–33.

Tyler, V. E. *The Honest Herbal.* Philadelphia: George F. Stickley, 1982.

Vestal, P. A.; and R. E. Schultes. *The Economic Botany of the Kiowa Indians.* Cambridge, Massachusetts: Botanical Museum, 1939.

Vogel, V. J. *American Indian Medicine.* New York: Ballantine Books, 1970.

Wada, K. N.; N. Ueda; H. Sawada; N. Amemiya, and M. Haga. "Inductive effects of bay leaf and its component costunolide on the mouse liver glutathione S-transferase." *Natural Medicines* 51, 3 (1997), 283–5.

Walker, W. *All the Plants of the Bible.* New York: Harper & Brothers, 1957.

Watt, J. M.; and M. G. Breyer-Brandwijk. *The Medicinal and Poisonous Plants of Southern and Eastern Africa,* 2nd ed. London: E. & S. Livingstone, 1962.

"The Wealth of India." *New Delhi: Council of Scientific and Industrial Research,* 1948–1976.

Wilder, L. B. *The Fragrant Garden: A Book about Sweet Scented Leaves and Flowers.* New York: Dover Publications, 1974.

Williamson, E. M.; and F. J. Evans. *Potter's New Cyclopaedia of Botanical Drugs and Preparations,* rev. ed. Essex, England: C. W. Daniel Co., 1988.

Zohry, M. *Plants of the Bible.* Cambridge, England: Cambridge University Press, 1982.

WEBSITES

S. M. Beckstrom-Sternberg; J. A. Duke; and K. K. Wain's The Ethnobotany Database **probe.nalusda.gov:8300/ cgi-bin/browse/ethnobotdb**

J. A. Duke's Father Nature's Farmacy; the Database **www.ars-grin.gov/dukw**

C. Hobbs' Herbs A–Z **www.allherb.com/consumer/AllHerb.com**

D. Hoffman's Health World Materia Medica **www.healthy.net/clinic/therapy/herbal/ herbic/herbs/index.html**

M. Moore's Dosages and Preparations **chili.rt66.com/hrbmoore/ ManualsMM/MatMed5.txt**

M. Moore's Specific Indication in Clinical Practice **chili.rt66.com/hrbmoore/ ManualsMM/SpecIndic3.txt**

Kathie Schmitt's Bible Study **www.muscanet.com/ -kschmitt/bibstdy.html**

Strong's Concordance **www.biblestudytools.net/Concordances/ StrongsExhaustiveConcordance**

Index